McGRAW-HILL READING

Spelling

Grade 2

Practice Book

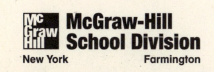

McGraw-Hill School Division

New York   Farmington

CONTENTS

Book 2.1/Unit 1

McGraw-Hill School Division

Book 2.1/Unit 2

McGraw-Hill School Division

Book 2.1/Unit 3

Book 2.2/Unit 1

Book 2.2 / Unit 2

McGraw-Hill School Division

Book 2.2 / Unit 3

McGraw-Hill School Division

Words with Short Vowels

Pretest Directions

Fold back your paper along the dotted line. Use the blanks to write each word as it is said to you. When you finish the test, unfold the paper and correct any spelling mistakes.

To Parents,
Here are the results of your child's weekly spelling Pretest. You can help your child study for the Posttest by following these simple steps for each word on the word list:

1. Read the word to your child.
2. Have your child write the word, saying each letter as it is written.
3. Say each letter of the word as your child checks the spelling.
4. If a mistake has been made, have your child read each letter of the correctly spelled word aloud, and then repeat steps 1–3.

1. _____ 1. still
2. _____ 2. best
3. _____ 3. bat
4. _____ 4. mom
5. _____ 5. just
6. _____ 6. desk
7. _____ 7. clock
8. _____ 8. hut
9. _____ 9. fit
10. _____ 10. plant

Challenge Words

_____ carrots
_____ crawls
_____ homework
_____ hurry
_____ lucky

Words with Short Vowels

Using the Word Study Steps

1. LOOK at the word.
2. SAY the word aloud.
3. STUDY the letters in the word.
4. WRITE the word.
5. CHECK the word.
   Did you spell the word right?
   If not, go back to step 1.

Spelling Tip

Short vowel sounds are usually spelled with a single vowel. Examples:

m**o**m, b**a**t

Word Scramble

Unscramble each set of letters to make a spelling word.

1. omm _____
2. kesd _____
3. tesb _____
4. tif _____
5. abt _____
6. tuh _____
7. ccolk _____
8. tanlp _____
9. tsuj _____
10. lilst _____

To Parents or Helpers:
Using the Word Study Steps above as your child comes across any new words will help him or her spell well. Review the steps as you both go over this week's spelling words.
Go over the Spelling Tip with your child. Ask him or her to spell other words that have short vowel sounds.
Help your child unscramble the letters to make the spelling words.

McGraw-Hill School Division

Words with Short Vowels

still	bat	just	clock	fit
best	mom	desk	hut	plant

Look at the spelling words in the box.

Write the spelling words that have the short **a** sound.

1. _____   2. _____

Write the spelling words that have the short **e** sound.

3. _____   4. _____

Write the spelling words that have the short **i** sound.

5. _____   6. _____

Write the spelling words that have the short **o** sound.

7. _____   8. _____

Write the spelling words that have the short **u** sound.

9. _____   10. _____

Puzzle

Solve the puzzle. Circle the five hidden spelling words.

p l a n t t i

f f i t h u t

b e s t s w t

c l o c k o f

McGraw-Hill School Division

Words with Short Vowels

still	bat	just	clock	fit
best	mom	desk	hut	plant

Fill in the Blanks

Write a spelling word to complete each sentence. Write
each word on the line.

1. Is your dress too small or does it _____?

2. I was _____ coming to find you.

3. Look at the _____ and tell me what time it is.

4. Bill hit the ball with the _____ .

Get Connected

Draw a line from each spelling word to its meaning.

5. best   female parent

6. still   better than all others

7. mom   not moving

What spelling word is the name of the picture?
Write it on the line below the picture.

8. _____   9. _____   10. _____

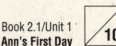

Words with Short Vowels

Find the Mistakes

Can you find the mistakes in these sentences? Circle the word in each sentence that is spelled incorrectly. Write it correctly on the line.

1. This is the bast party I ever had! _____

2. Hit the ball with the batt. _____

3. This hat does not fiet on my head. _____

4. The hutt was made of straw and mud. _____

5. The klock is on the wall. _____

Proofreading Activity

Read the story. There are five spelling mistakes. Circle each mistake. Then write the correct word on the line.

Nora was sitting at her desc one day. She saw a butterfly jost outside her window. It was resting on a green plante. Nora sat very stell until the butterfly flew away. Then she ran to tell her momm.

6. _____   7. _____   8. _____

9. _____ 10. _____

Writing Activity

Look out a window. Write a few sentences describing what you can see. Use two spelling words.

_____

_____

_____

Words with Short Vowels

Look at the words in each set. One word in each set is spelled correctly. Use a pencil to color in the circle in front of that word.
Before you begin, look at the sample sets of words. Sample A has been done for you. Do Sample B by yourself. When you are sure you know what to do, you may go on with the rest of the page.

Sample A
Ⓐ stup
Ⓑ shtop
Ⓒ stop
Ⓓ stopp

Sample B
Ⓔ homm
Ⓕ humm
Ⓖ hume
Ⓗ home

1. Ⓐ palnt
   Ⓑ plant
   Ⓒ plannt
   Ⓓ plante

2. Ⓔ stil
   Ⓕ stiel
   Ⓖ still
   Ⓗ sitll

3. Ⓐ desk
   Ⓑ deks
   Ⓒ desc
   Ⓓ deske

4. Ⓔ momm
   Ⓕ mome
   Ⓖ moom
   Ⓗ mom

5. Ⓐ clock
   Ⓑ clok
   Ⓒ cloc
   Ⓓ colck

6. Ⓔ fitt
   Ⓕ fite
   Ⓖ fti
   Ⓗ fit

7. Ⓐ hutte
   Ⓑ hut
   Ⓒ hutt
   Ⓓ hute

8. Ⓔ jus
   Ⓕ juste
   Ⓖ jusst
   Ⓗ just

9. Ⓐ batt
   Ⓑ bat
   Ⓒ baet
   Ⓓ batte

10. Ⓔ beste
    Ⓕ best
    Ⓖ bset
    Ⓗ bist

Words with Long Vowels

Pretest Directions

Fold back your paper along the dotted line.
Use the blanks to write each word as it is said to you. When you finish the test, unfold the paper and correct any spelling mistakes.

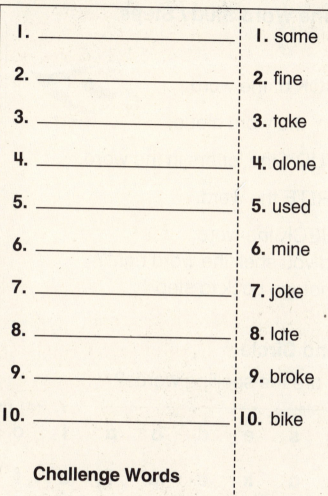

1. _____	**1.** same
2. _____	**2.** fine
3. _____	**3.** take
4. _____	**4.** alone
5. _____	**5.** used
6. _____	**6.** mine
7. _____	**7.** joke
8. _____	**8.** late
9. _____	**9.** broke
10. _____	**10.** bike

Challenge Words

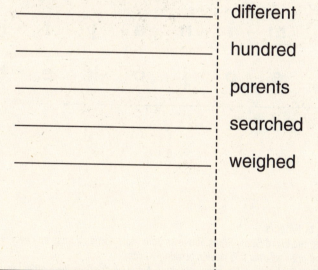

_____	different
_____	hundred
_____	parents
_____	searched
_____	weighed

To Parents,

Here are the results of your child's weekly spelling Pretest. You can help your child study for the Posttest by following these simple steps for each word on the word list:

1. Read the word to your child.

2. Have your child write the word, saying each letter as it is written.

3. Say each letter of the word as your child checks the spelling.

4. If a mistake has been made, have your child read each letter of the correctly spelled word aloud, and then repeat steps 1–3.

Words with Long Vowels

Using the Word Study Steps

1. LOOK at the word.

2. SAY the word aloud.

3. STUDY the letters in the word.

4. WRITE the word.

5. CHECK the word.
   Did you spell the word right?
   If not, go back to step 1.

Spelling Tip

In words with the pattern vowel-consonant-silent **e**, the silent **e** makes the vowel sound long. Don't forget the silent **e**.
Examples:
   take   fine   joke

Find and Circle

Where are the spelling words?

u	s	e	d	b	a	l	o	n	e	c	b
t	a	k	e	m	l	a	f	i	n	e	i
s	m	i	n	e	j	t	h	g	e	d	k
r	e	p	j	o	k	e	b	r	o	k	e

To Parents or Helpers:

Using the Word Study Steps above as your child comes across any new words will help him or her spell well. Review the steps as you both go over this week's spelling words.

Go over the Spelling Tip with your child. Ask if he or she knows other words with the vowel-consonant-silent e pattern.

Help your child find and circle the spelling words in the puzzle.

Book 2.1/Unit 1
Henry and Mudge
10

McGraw-Hill School Division

Words with Long Vowels

same	take	used	joke	broke
fine	alone	mine	late	bike

Look at the spelling words in the box.
Write the spelling words that have the long **a** sound.

I. _____ 2. _____ 3. _____

Write the spelling words that have the long **i** sound.

4. _____ 5. _____ 6. _____

Write the spelling words that have the long **o** sound.

7. _____ 8. _____ 9. _____

Write the spelling word that has the long **u** sound.

10. _____

Misfit Letter

An extra letter has been added to the spelling words. Draw a line through the letter that does not belong and write the word correctly on the line.

II. m y i n e _____ 12. h u s e d _____

13. t a c k e _____ 14. a l o a n e _____

15. f e i n e _____ 16. s a h m e _____

17. b i c k e _____ 18. j o w k e _____

19. b r o u k e _____ 20. l a e t e _____

Words with Long Vowels

same	take	used	joke	broke
fine	alone	mine	late	bike

Fill in the Blanks

Write the spelling word that completes each sentence.

1. You can play with friends, or you can play _____.

2. You can tell a sad story, or you can tell a _____.

3. You can walk to the store, or you can ride your _____.

4. This car is new, but that one is _____.

Opposite and Alike

Write the spelling word that means **the opposite** of each word below.

5. yours _____

6. early _____

7. fixed _____

Write the spelling word that means **the same** as each word below.

8. grab _____

9. good _____

10. alike _____

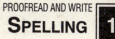
Words with Long Vowels

Proofreading Activity

There are five spelling mistakes in the story below. Circle each misspelled word. Write the words correctly on the lines below.

Pedro was riding his biek one day. He did not want to ride alon. He asked Mike to join him. When Pedro's wheel broce, his bike would not go. It was too laet to get a new wheel from the bike shop. Pedro had to taake his bike home.

1. _____

2. _____

3. _____

4. _____

5. _____

Writing Activity

Write a list of ways to be safe with your bike. Use three spelling words in your list.

_____

_____

_____

_____

_____

Words with Long Vowels

Look at the words in each set. One word in each set is spelled
correctly. Use a pencil to color in the circle in front of that word.
Before you begin, look at the sample sets of words. Sample A has
been done for you. Do Sample B by yourself. When you are sure you
know what to do, you may go on with the rest of the page.

Sample A
- Ⓐ linne
- Ⓑ lin
- Ⓒ line
- Ⓓ liine

Sample B
- Ⓔ mom
- Ⓕ moom
- Ⓖ momm
- Ⓗ mome

1. Ⓐ takk
   Ⓑ take
   Ⓒ taek
   Ⓓ tacke

2. Ⓔ latte
   Ⓕ lat
   Ⓖ late
   Ⓗ latt

3. Ⓐ joke
   Ⓑ joce
   Ⓒ jocke
   Ⓓ jook

4. Ⓔ bik
   Ⓕ bicke
   Ⓖ bice
   Ⓗ bike

5. Ⓐ mimm
   Ⓑ myne
   Ⓒ mien
   Ⓓ mine

6. Ⓔ usd
   Ⓕ used
   Ⓖ ussed
   Ⓗ ysed

7. Ⓐ alon
   Ⓑ alone
   Ⓒ alonne
   Ⓓ aloan

8. Ⓔ samm
   Ⓕ same
   Ⓖ saem
   Ⓗ saym

9. Ⓐ brock
   Ⓑ brok
   Ⓒ broke
   Ⓓ broce

10. Ⓔ fine
    Ⓕ finne
    Ⓖ fien
    Ⓗ fyne

McGraw-Hill School Division

Words with Long *a* and Long *e*

Pretest Directions

Fold back your paper along the dotted line.
Use the blanks to write each word as it is said to you. When you finish the test, unfold the paper and correct any spelling mistakes.

To Parents,

Here are the results of your child's weekly spelling Pretest. You can help your child study for the Posttest by following these simple steps for each word on the word list:

1. Read the word to your child.

2. Have your child write the word, saying each letter as it is written.

3. Say each letter of the word as your child checks the spelling.

4. If a mistake has been made, have your child read each letter of the correctly spelled word aloud, and then repeat steps 1–3.

1. _____ 1. stay
2. _____ 2. plain
3. _____ 3. seat
4. _____ 4. green
5. _____ 5. keep
6. _____ 6. chief
7. _____ 7. mail
8. _____ 8. dream
9. _____ 9. clay
10. _____ 10. mean

Challenge Words

_____ answered
_____ grandmother
_____ idea
_____ remember
_____ serious

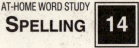
Words with Long *a* and Long *e*

Using the Word Study Steps

1. LOOK at the word.
2. SAY the word aloud.
3. STUDY the letters in the word.
4. WRITE the word.
5. CHECK the word.
   Did you spell the word right?
   If not, go back to step 1.

Spelling Tip

When a base word ends with a vowel followed by a **y**, do not change the ending when adding suffixes or endings. Example:

stay → stayed

X the Words

Put an X on the words with the long **e** sound.

clay	mean	mail	seat	stay
mail	stay	chief	plain	dream
plain	green	clay	keep	mail

To Parents or Helpers:

Using the Word Study Steps above as your child comes across any new words will help him or her spell well. Review the steps as you both go over this week's spelling words.

Go over the Spelling Tip with your child. Ask him or her how many spelling words follow this rule and how many don't. Help your child find words with the long e sound.

McGraw-Hill School Division

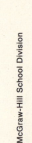

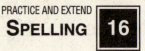

McGraw-Hill School Division

Words with Long *a* and Long *e*

stay	seat	keep	mail	clay
plain	green	chief	dream	mean

Write the Words

Write the spelling words that have long **a** spelled **ai**.

1. _____ 2. _____

Write the spelling words that have long **a** spelled **ay**.

3. _____ 4. _____

Write the spelling words that have long **e** spelled **ea**.

5. _____ 6. _____

7. _____

Write the spelling words that have long **e** spelled **ee**.

8. _____ 9. _____

Write the spelling word that has long **e** spelled **ie**.

10. _____

Sounds the Same

Write a spelling word that rhymes with the two words in each group.

11. deep   jeep   _____

12. train   rain   _____

13. meat   heat   _____

14. cream   stream   _____

15. sail   tail   _____

McGraw-Hill School Division

Words with Long *a* and Long *e*

stay	seat	keep	mail	clay
plain	green	chief	dream	mean

Match-Ups

Draw a line from each spelling word to its meaning.

1. seat   not fancy

2. green   what you do when you sleep

3. mean   what you sit on

4. dream   not very nice

5. stay   wait in one place; not leave

6. plain   a color

Sentences to Complete

Write a spelling word on each line to complete the sentence.

7. I sat on the back _____ of the bus.

8. I shaped the _____ with my hands.

9. You cannot _____ a letter without a stamp.

10. The fire _____ rode on the red truck.

11. Will you give the puppy away, or will you _____ it?

12. Last night I had a strange _____.

Words with Long *a* and Long *e*

Proofreading Activity

There is one spelling mistake in each sentence below.
Circle each misspelled word. Write the words correctly on
the lines below.

1. The leaf on the plant is grean. _____

2. The jar is made of clai. _____

3. I put the letter in the mial. _____

4. What did you sey to the teacher? _____

5. The cheef was first to the fire. _____

6. Once, I had a dreem about ice cream. _____

7. He likes to sit on the last saet of the bus. _____

Writing Activity

Three of this week's spelling words end with the same
letter. Write a sentence using each word.

_____

_____

_____

_____

_____

Words with Long *a* and Long *e*

Look at the words in each set. One word in each set is spelled correctly. Use a pencil to color in the circle in front of that word. Before you begin, look at the sample sets of words. Sample A has been done for you. Do Sample B by yourself. When you are sure you know what to do, you may go on with the rest of the page.

Sample A
Ⓐ sial
Ⓑ sael
Ⓒ sail
Ⓓ sayl

Sample B
Ⓔ bik
Ⓕ bike
Ⓖ bice
Ⓗ biek

1. Ⓐ maile
   Ⓑ mail
   Ⓒ mayl
   Ⓓ maill

2. Ⓔ plain
   Ⓕ plian
   Ⓖ playn
   Ⓗ plean

3. Ⓐ mean
   Ⓑ meen
   Ⓒ maen
   Ⓓ meane

4. Ⓔ seet
   Ⓕ seat
   Ⓖ sete
   Ⓗ saet

5. Ⓐ cheif
   Ⓑ chief
   Ⓒ cheef
   Ⓓ cheaf

6. Ⓔ gren
   Ⓕ grien
   Ⓖ green
   Ⓗ grean

7. Ⓐ dreme
   Ⓑ dreem
   Ⓒ dream
   Ⓓ draem

8. Ⓔ stey
   Ⓕ stai
   Ⓖ stae
   Ⓗ stay

9. Ⓐ claiy
   Ⓑ clay
   Ⓒ cley
   Ⓓ clai

10. Ⓔ kepe
    Ⓕ kiep
    Ⓖ keap
    Ⓗ keep

McGraw-Hill School Division

Words with Long *o* and Long *i*

Pretest Directions

Fold back your paper along the dotted line.
Use the blanks to write each word as it is said to you. When you finish the test, unfold the paper and correct any spelling mistakes.

1. _____
2. _____
3. _____
4. _____
5. _____
6. _____
7. _____
8. _____
9. _____
10. _____

1. toe
2. slow
3. old
4. mind
5. by
6. follow
7. dry
8. load
9. row
10. sigh

Challenge Words

_____ broken

_____ carefully

_____ cattle

_____ gently

_____ safety

To Parents,

Here are the results of your child's weekly spelling Pretest. You can help your child study for the Posttest by following these simple steps for each word on the word list:

1. Read the word to your child.

2. Have your child write the word, saying each letter as it is written.

3. Say each letter of the word as your child checks the spelling.

4. If a mistake has been made, have your child read each letter of the correctly spelled word aloud, and then repeat steps 1–3.

McGraw-Hill School Division

Words with Long *o* and Long *i*

Using the Word Study Steps

1. LOOK at the word.

2. SAY the word aloud.

3. STUDY the letters in the word.

4. WRITE the word.

5. CHECK the word.
   Did you spell the word right?
   If not, go back to step 1.

Spelling Tip

You learned that a long vowel sound is often spelled with two vowels. But there are exceptions. Which spelling words have long vowels spelled with two letters? Which have long vowels spelled with one letter?

Circle the Word

Circle the words with the long **o** sound.

toe	slow	old	mind	by
follow	dry	load	row	sigh

To Parents or Helpers:

Using the Word Study Steps above as your child comes across any new words will help him or her spell well. Review the steps as you both go over this week's spelling words.

Go over the Spelling Tip with your child. Ask your child to sound out each spelling word to figure out which ones have long vowels spelled with one letter.

Help your child find and circle words with long **o** in the puzzle.

Words with Long *o* and Long *i*

toe	old	by	dry	row
slow	mind	follow	load	sigh

Write the Word

Write the spelling word that has long **o** spelled **oa**.

1. _____

Write the spelling word that has long **o** spelled **oe**.

2. _____

Write the spelling words that have long **o** spelled **ow**.

3. _____   4. _____

5. _____

Write the spelling word that has long **o** spelled **o**.

6. _____

Write the spelling word that has long **i** spelled **i**.

7. _____

Write the spelling words that have long **i** spelled **y**.

8. _____   9. _____

Write the spelling word that has long **i** spelled **igh**.

10. _____

New Words

Make a new word from the spelling list by changing the first letter.

11. road – r + l _____   14. find – f + m _____

12. cry – c + d _____   15. hoe – h + t _____

13. high – h + s _____

McGraw-Hill School Division

Words with Long *o* and Long *i*

toe	old	by	dry	row
slow	mind	follow	load	sigh

Opposites

Draw a line to connect the words that mean the opposite.

1. dry   fast

2. old   wet

3. slow   young

Finish the Sentence

Look at the picture. Write the spelling word to complete each sentence below.

4. Do you _____
   if I sit with you?

5. We live in a house _____
   the river.

6. I banged my big _____
   on the step.

McGraw-Hill School Division

Words with Long *o* and Long *i*

Proofreading Activity

There is one spelling mistake in each sentence below. Circle each misspelled word. Write the correct spelling word on the line.

1. Will you help me lode the car? _____

2. I heard Mom sihe. _____

3. We found an oled coin at the beach. _____

4. Your towe is a part of your foot. _____

5. Beans grow in a roe. _____

Writing Activity

Write some important rules for a class trip to the park. Use three spelling words in your rules.

_____

_____

_____

_____

Words with Long *o* and Long *i*

Look at the words in each set. One word in each set is spelled correctly. Use a pencil to color in the circle in front of that word. Before you begin, look at the sample sets of words. Sample A has been done for you. Do Sample B by yourself. When you are sure you know what to do, you may go on with the rest of the page.

Sample A
- Ⓐ fri
- Ⓑ frey
- ● fry
- Ⓓ frigh

Sample B
- Ⓔ dreem
- Ⓕ draem
- Ⓖ dreme
- Ⓗ dream

1. Ⓐ dry
   Ⓑ dri
   Ⓒ drigh
   Ⓓ drie

2. Ⓔ laod
   Ⓕ lowd
   Ⓖ load
   Ⓗ lood

3. Ⓐ roo
   Ⓑ ro
   Ⓒ row
   Ⓓ roa

4. Ⓔ mynd
   Ⓕ midn
   Ⓖ mind
   Ⓗ miend

5. Ⓐ biy
   Ⓑ bi
   Ⓒ bigh
   Ⓓ by

6. Ⓔ toe
   Ⓕ tooe
   Ⓖ towe
   Ⓗ toow

7. Ⓐ sigh
   Ⓑ si
   Ⓒ sy
   Ⓓ sihg

8. Ⓔ follo
   Ⓕ foolow
   Ⓖ follow
   Ⓗ folow

9. Ⓐ owld
   Ⓑ odl
   Ⓒ olde
   Ⓓ old

10. Ⓔ slowe
    Ⓕ sloow
    Ⓖ slow
    Ⓗ sloa

Name _____ Date _____

Name _____ Date _____

Name _____ Date _____

Words from Social Studies

Pretest Directions

Fold back your paper along the dotted line. Use the blanks to write each word as it is said to you. When you finish the test, unfold the paper and correct any spelling mistakes.

To Parents,

Here are the results of your child's weekly spelling Pretest. You can help your child study for the Posttest by following these simple steps for each word on the word list:

1. Read the word to your child.

2. Have your child write the word, saying each letter as it is written.

3. Say each letter of the word as your child checks the spelling.

4. If a mistake has been made, have your child read each letter of the correctly spelled word aloud, and then repeat steps 1–3.

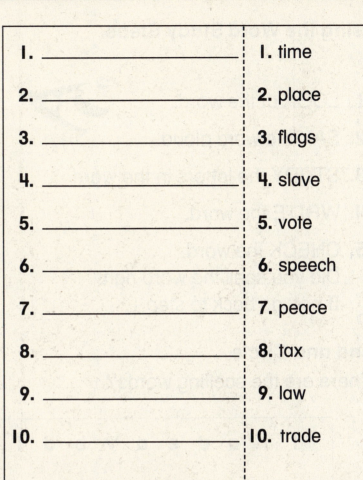

1. _____   **1.** time
2. _____   **2.** place
3. _____   **3.** flags
4. _____   **4.** slave
5. _____   **5.** vote
6. _____   **6.** speech
7. _____   **7.** peace
8. _____   **8.** tax
9. _____   **9.** law
10. _____   **10.** trade

Challenge Words

_____   artist
_____   body
_____   famous
_____   hour
_____   visit

Words from Social Studies

Using the Word Study Steps

1. LOOK at the word.

2. SAY the word aloud.

3. STUDY the letters in the word.

4. WRITE the word.

5. CHECK the word.
   Did you spell the word right?
   If not, go back to step 1.

<table>
<tr><td>

Spelling Tip

Keep a Personal Word List in a notebook. Write words you have trouble spelling.

</td></tr>
</table>

Find and Circle

Where are the spelling words?

t	r	a	d	e	a	v	b	d	f	l	a	g	s	b
i	p	l	a	c	e	o	j	s	l	a	v	e	c	h
m	f	h	g	n	p	t	a	x	q	w	y	f	z	o
e	r	s	s	p	e	e	c	h	u	p	e	a	c	e

To Parents or Helpers:

Using the Word Study Steps above as your child comes across any new words will help him or her spell well. Review the steps as you both go over this week's spelling words.

Go over the Spelling Tip with your child. Help him or her get started in developing a Personal Word List.

Help your child find and circle the spelling words in the puzzle.

McGraw-Hill School Division

Words from Social Studies

time	flags	vote	peace	law
place	slave	speech	tax	trade

Find the Pattern

Write the spelling words that have each spelling pattern.

Words beginning with **p**

1. _____ 2. _____

Words beginning with **s**

3. _____ 4. _____

Words beginning with **t**

5. _____ 6. _____

7. _____

Words beginning with other letters

8. _____ 9. _____

10. _____

Word Puzzle

Find and circle six spelling words in the puzzle. Words can be found up and down and across.

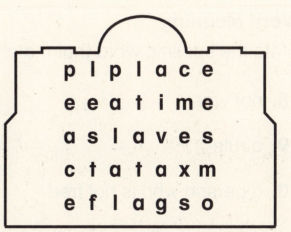

```
p l p l a c e
e e a t i m e
a s l a v e s
c t a t a x m
e f l a g s o
```

McGraw-Hill School Division

Words from Social Studies

time	flags	vote	peace	law
place	slave	speech	tax	trade

All in a Set

Write a spelling word to complete each sentence.

1. We pay a _____ on things we buy.

2. What _____ will we meet?

3. If you _____ for her she might win.

4. She will give a _____ in school today.

5. School is the _____ where we learn.

6. Will you _____ your toy for mine?

7. We waved the _____ and marched in the parade.

Word Meaning

Write the spelling word that matches each clue below.

8. not war _____

9. a rule _____

10. a person who is not free _____

McGraw-Hill School Division

Words from Social Studies

Proofreading Activity

There are six spelling mistakes in the paragraph below. Circle each misspelled word. Write the words correctly on the lines below.

What is this? I see flages flying from the poles. If you stay in this plais you will be able to see. The man made a spech and said, "Voet for me!" He says that we need a new tacks. It is timm to go home.

1. _____   2. _____

3. _____   4. _____

5. _____   6. _____

Writing Activity

Look up four of your spelling words in a dictionary. Write each word in your Word Journal, along with its meaning.

_____

_____

_____

_____

_____

Words from Social Studies

Look at the words in each set. One word in each set is spelled correctly. Use a pencil to color in the circle in front of that word. Before you begin, look at the sample sets of words. Sample A has been done for you. Do Sample B by yourself. When you are sure you know what to do, you may go on with the rest of the page.

Sample A
- (A) mape
- (B) map
- (C) mapp
- (D) mappe

Sample B
- (E) lowd
- (F) load
- (G) lowed
- (H) laod

1.
- (A) timme
- (B) time
- (C) timm
- (D) tyme

2.
- (E) slave
- (F) slav
- (G) slaev
- (H) slayv

3.
- (A) flaggs
- (B) fligs
- (C) flages
- (D) flags

4.
- (E) tasx
- (F) tax
- (G) tacs
- (H) taks

5.
- (A) voot
- (B) voat
- (C) vote
- (D) vot

6.
- (E) trad
- (F) traid
- (G) traed
- (H) trade

7.
- (A) plase
- (B) place
- (C) plas
- (D) plese

8.
- (E) speche
- (F) speach
- (G) spech
- (H) speech

9.
- (A) lawe
- (B) lau
- (C) lauw
- (D) law

10.
- (E) peace
- (F) peece
- (G) pese
- (H) peese

McGraw-Hill School Division

Book 2.1/Unit 1 Review Test

Read each sentence. If an underlined word is spelled wrong,
fill in the circle that goes with that word. If no word is spelled
wrong, fill in the circle below NONE.
Read Sample A, and do Sample B.

A. The <u>feild</u> of <u>grain</u> is <u>ripe</u>.
     A   B   C

NONE
A. Ⓐ Ⓑ Ⓒ Ⓓ

B. Did you <u>find</u> the <u>game</u> <u>today</u>?
          E   F   G

NONE
B. Ⓔ Ⓕ Ⓖ Ⓗ

1. <u>Just</u> <u>follow</u> me to my <u>desck</u>.
   A   B   C

NONE
1. Ⓐ Ⓑ Ⓒ Ⓓ

2. Go <u>alone</u> and take your <u>bat</u> and <u>byke</u>.
       E   F   G

NONE
2. Ⓔ Ⓕ Ⓖ Ⓗ

3. The <u>cheef</u> will <u>follow</u> him <u>alone</u>.
     A   B   C

NONE
3. Ⓐ Ⓑ Ⓒ Ⓓ

4. I <u>used</u> the <u>taks</u> book on your <u>desk</u>.
    E   F   G

NONE
4. Ⓔ Ⓕ Ⓖ Ⓗ

5. The <u>grean</u> <u>clay</u> is too <u>dry</u>.
      A   B   C

NONE
5. Ⓐ Ⓑ Ⓒ Ⓓ

6. Will you <u>traid</u> a <u>bat</u> for a <u>bike</u>?
         E   F   G

NONE
6. Ⓔ Ⓕ Ⓖ Ⓗ

7. Find a <u>dry</u> <u>place</u> to sit <u>alone</u> and fish.
        A   B   C

NONE
7. Ⓐ Ⓑ Ⓒ Ⓓ

8. Do you <u>mind</u> if I <u>plase</u> a loud <u>clock</u> here?
        E   F   G

NONE
8. Ⓔ Ⓕ Ⓖ Ⓗ

9. Make a pot with the <u>saym</u> <u>clay</u> I <u>used</u>.
              A   B   C

NONE
9. Ⓐ Ⓑ Ⓒ Ⓓ

Go on

Book 2.1/Unit 1 Review Test

10. My <u>desk</u> <u>clok</u> woke me from my <u>dream</u>.
      E   F   G

10. Ⓔ Ⓕ Ⓖ Ⓗ NONE

11. In my <u>dream</u> I was <u>chief</u> of the <u>place</u>.
         A   B   C

11. Ⓐ Ⓑ Ⓒ Ⓓ NONE

12. The sales <u>tax</u> <u>alone</u> was <u>just</u> too high.
             E   F   G

12. Ⓔ Ⓕ Ⓖ Ⓗ NONE

13. I don't <u>mined</u> the <u>bat</u> in the <u>clock</u> tower.
            A   B   C

13. Ⓐ Ⓑ Ⓒ Ⓓ NONE

14. I'll <u>gust</u> make the <u>same</u> <u>trade</u>.
          E   F   G

14. Ⓔ Ⓕ Ⓖ Ⓗ NONE

15. <u>Place</u> one <u>towe</u> in the cold, <u>green</u> lake.
        A   B   C

15. Ⓐ Ⓑ Ⓒ Ⓓ NONE

16. My <u>chief</u> goal is to buy the <u>same</u> <u>bike</u>.
          E   F   G

16. Ⓔ Ⓕ Ⓖ Ⓗ NONE

17. I will <u>place</u> the <u>clay</u> ball in my <u>desk</u>.
            A   B   C

17. Ⓐ Ⓑ Ⓒ Ⓓ NONE

18. The <u>slav</u> <u>trade</u> was <u>just</u> not right to do.
           E   F   G

18. Ⓔ Ⓕ Ⓖ Ⓗ NONE

19. We'll <u>folow</u> the <u>slave</u> to the <u>green</u> shack.
           A   B   C

19. Ⓐ Ⓑ Ⓒ Ⓓ NONE

20. In a <u>dream</u>, a tiger-shaped <u>clock</u> bit my <u>toe</u>.
          E   F   G

20. Ⓔ Ⓕ Ⓖ Ⓗ NONE

Words with /ü/ *oo, ue, ew*

Pretest Directions

Fold back your paper along the dotted line. Use the blanks to write each word as it is said to you. When you finish the test, unfold the paper, and correct any spelling mistakes. Practice those words for the Posttest.

To Parents,

Here are the results of your child's weekly spelling Pretest. You can help your child study for the Posttest by following these simple steps for each word on the word list:

1. Read the word to your child.

2. Have your child write the word, saying each letter as it is written.

3. Say each letter of the word as your child checks the spelling.

4. If a mistake has been made, have your child read each letter of the correctly spelled word aloud and then repeat steps 1–3.

1. _____	1. true
2. _____	2. too
3. _____	3. new
4. _____	4. room
5. _____	5. blew
6. _____	6. tool
7. _____	7. clue
8. _____	8. boot
9. _____	9. few
10. _____	10. school

Challenge Words

_____	announced
_____	empty
_____	poured
_____	squeezed
_____	wrong

Name _____ Date _____

Words with /ü/oo, ue, ew

Using the Word Study Steps

1. LOOK at the word.

2. SAY the word aloud.

3. STUDY the letters in the word.

4. WRITE the word.

5. CHECK the word.
   Did you spell the word right?
   If not, go back to step 1.

Spelling Tip

Think of a word that rhymes with the new word. Rhyming words often have the same spelling pattern.
Example:
   c + ool = cool
   t + ool = tool

Crossword Puzzle

Write the spelling word that best matches each clue. Put the spelling words in the boxes that start with the same number.

CROSSWORD CLUES

ACROSS

2. right
3. heavy shoe
5. place for learning
7. space
8. not old

DOWN

1. not many
2. also
3. puffed, like the wind
4. a hammer is one
6. hint

To Parents or Helpers:
    Using the Word Study Steps above as your child comes across any new words will help him or her spell well. Review the steps as you both go over this week's spelling words.
    Go over the Spelling Tip with your child. Ask for other words that rhyme with the spelling words.
    Help your child complete the crossword puzzle.

Words with /ü/ *oo, ue, ew*

true	new	blew	clue	few
too	room	tool	boot	school

Match each word with a spelling pattern. Write the spelling word on the line.

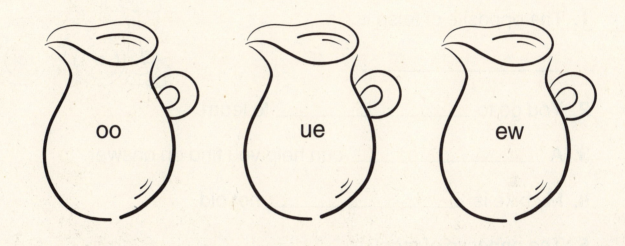

oo   **ue**   **ew**

1. _____   6. _____   8. _____

2. _____   7. _____   9. _____

3. _____   10. _____

4. _____

5. _____

Name _____ Date _____

Words with /ü/ *oo, ue, ew*

true	new	blew	clue	few
too	room	tool	boot	school

Fill It In

Complete each sentence with a spelling word.

I. The opposite of false is

_____ .

2. You go to _____ to learn.

3. A _____ can help you find an answer.

4. My bike is _____, not old.

5. The opposite of many is _____.

6. Dad makes me clean my _____ once a week.

7. The wind _____ the trees down last night.

8. Linda is very bright, and a good worker _____.

Word Building

Be a word builder. Build new words that mean more than one by adding the letter s.

9. room + s = _____

10. clue + s = _____

II. boot + s = _____

12. tool + s = _____

Challenge Extension: Scramble the challenge words and write them on the board. Have students unscramble the words.

36

Book 2.1/Unit 2
Lemonade for Sale 12

McGraw-Hill School Division

Words with /ü/ *oo, ue, ew*

Proofreading Activity

There are six spelling mistakes in the letter below. Circle each misspelled word. Write the words correctly on the lines below.

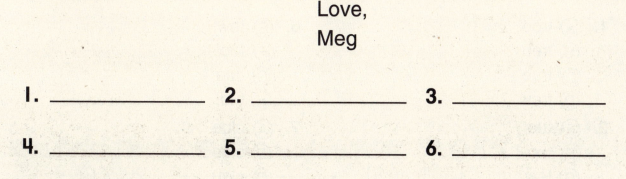

Dear Grandma,

You should see our clubhouse. We fixed it up, and the big rewm now looks noo! Mom gave us a fue tewls to use. Danny painted the walls. Matthew and I helped, tew. I can't wait until you visit, so you can see that this is all troo.

Love,
Meg

1. _____ 2. _____ 3. _____

4. _____ 5. _____ 6. _____

Writing Activity

Write sentences about things you like to do outside. Use four spelling words in your sentences. Circle the spelling words you use.

_____

_____

_____

_____

Words with /ü/ *oo, ue, ew*

Look at the words in each set. One word in each set is spelled
correctly. Use a pencil to color in the circle in front of that word.
Before you begin, look at the sample sets of words. Sample A has
been done for you. Do Sample B by yourself. When you are sure you
know what to do, you may go on with the rest of the page.

Sample A
- Ⓐ backe
- Ⓑ bac
- Ⓒ back
- Ⓓ bakke

Sample B
- Ⓔ dance
- Ⓕ danz
- Ⓖ dansce
- Ⓗ dants

1. Ⓐ troo
   Ⓑ treu
   Ⓒ true
   Ⓓ trew

2. Ⓔ tue
   Ⓕ too
   Ⓖ tew
   Ⓗ tou

3. Ⓐ noo
   Ⓑ nue
   Ⓒ nou
   Ⓓ new

4. Ⓔ room
   Ⓕ ruem
   Ⓖ rewm
   Ⓗ rume

5. Ⓐ bloo
   Ⓑ blew
   Ⓒ bleu
   Ⓓ bluo

6. Ⓔ tewl
   Ⓕ tool
   Ⓖ tule
   Ⓗ tuel

7. Ⓐ clue
   Ⓑ cloo
   Ⓒ cleu
   Ⓓ clew

8. Ⓔ beut
   Ⓕ bewt
   Ⓖ boot
   Ⓗ buet

9. Ⓐ fue
   Ⓑ fwe
   Ⓒ fuw
   Ⓓ few

10. Ⓔ schewl
    Ⓕ school
    Ⓖ schule
    Ⓗ schole

McGraw-Hill School Division

Book 2.1/Unit 2
Lemonade for Sale 10

Words with /ou/ *-ou*, *-ow*; and /oi/ *-oi*, *-oy*

Pretest Directions

Fold back your paper along the dotted line. Use the blanks to write each word as it is said to you. When you finish the test, unfold the paper, and correct any spelling mistakes. Practice those words for the Posttest.

To Parents,

Here are the results of your child's weekly spelling Pretest. You can help your child study for the Posttest by following these simple steps for each word on the word list:

1. Read the word to your child.

2. Have your child write the word, saying each letter as it is written.

3. Say each letter of the word as your child checks the spelling.

4. If a mistake has been made, have your child read each letter of the correctly spelled word aloud and then repeat steps 1–3.

1. _____	1. down
2. _____	2. out
3. _____	3. point
4. _____	4. joy
5. _____	5. house
6. _____	6. now
7. _____	7. coin
8. _____	8. loud
9. _____	9. brown
10. _____	10. cowboy

Challenge Words

_____	candles
_____	glanced
_____	repeated
_____	special
_____	wild

Words with /ou/ *ow*, *ou* and /oi/ *oi*, *oy*

Using the Word Study Steps

1. LOOK at the word.

2. SAY the word aloud.

3. STUDY the letters in the word.

4. WRITE the word.

5. CHECK the word.
   Did you spell the word right?
   If not, go back to step 1.

Spelling Tip

Break the word into word parts or syllables.
Example:
  cow + boy = cowboy

Find and Circle

Where are the spelling words?

v	d	o	w	n	x	p	o	i	n	t	c
c	o	i	n	b	h	j	b	r	o	w	n
l	o	u	d	l	h	o	u	s	e	u	o
x	c	o	w	b	o	y	v	o	u	t	w

To Parents or Helpers:
    Using the Word Study Steps above as your child comes across any new words will help him or her spell well. Review the steps as you both go over this week's spelling words.
    Go over each Spelling Tip with your child. Help your child break other words into word parts or syllables.
    Help your child find and circle the spelling words in the puzzle.

McGraw-Hill School Division

Words with /ou/ -ou, -ow; and /oi/ -oi, -oy

down	point	house	coin	brown
out	joy	now	loud	cowboy

Mail a Letter

Fill in the blanks below with spelling words that match each spelling pattern. One word will be used twice!

ou   **oy**   **oi**   **ow**

1. _____   4. _____   6. _____   8. _____

2. _____   5. _____   7. _____   9. _____

3. _____   10. _____

                                                            11. _____

Spelling Patterns

Which spelling of /oi/ is usually found at the end of a word or syllable?

12. _____

Which spelling of /oi/ is found in the middle of a word?

13. _____

Which spelling of /ou/ may appear at the end of a word or syllable?

14. _____

Which spelling of /ou/ appears at the beginning or in the middle of a word?

15. _____

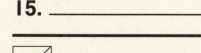

Words with /ou/ -ou, -ow; and /oi/ -oi, -oy

down	point	house	coin	brown
out	joy	now	loud	cowboy

Write the spelling word to complete each sentence below.

1. Peter had a birthday party at his _____.

2. His mom gave him a pair of

   _____ boots.

3. The toe of each boot came to a sharp _____.

4. Sam gave Peter an old silver _____.

5. Peter's mom brought out a dark _____ chocolate cake.

6. There was a _____ shout of "Happy Birthday!"

7. "Blow the candles _____," said his mom.

8. Peter blew so hard the candles fell _____.

9. "Let's eat right _____," said Peter.

10. The house was filled with happiness and _____.

Word Building

Be a word builder. Put the words together. Write the new words you can make.

11. dog + house = _____ 12. out + side = _____

McGraw-Hill School Division

Challenge Extension: Have children make up a little story using as many of the challenge words as they can.

Book 2.1/Unit 2
A Letter to Amy
12

Words with /ou/ -ou, -ow; and /oi/ -oi, -oy

Proofreading Activity

There are six spelling mistakes in the party invitation below. Circle each misspelled word. Write the words correctly on the lines below.

Please come to my birthday party on Friday. Come as soon as school is owt. I live in a broun howse on First Street. A real cowboi will be there. He will do rope tricks and sing lowd songs. We'll have ice cream and cake. Bring this lucky coyne, and you might win a special prize!

1. _____   2. _____   3. _____

4. _____   5. _____   6. _____

Writing Activity

Write a short story about what Peter's party was like. Use four of the spelling words in your story. Circle the spelling words you use.

_____

_____

_____

_____

_____

Words with /ou/ -ou, -ow; and /oi/ -oi, -oy

Look at the words in each set. One word in each set is spelled correctly. Use a pencil to color in the circle in front of that word. Before you begin, look at the sample sets of words. Sample A has been done for you. Do Sample B by yourself. When you are sure you know what to do, you may go on with the rest of the page.

Sample A
- Ⓐ onlee
- Ⓑ onley
- Ⓒ only
- Ⓓ onely

Sample B
- Ⓔ teche
- Ⓕ teech
- Ⓖ teach
- Ⓗ taech

1.
- Ⓐ now
- Ⓑ noow
- Ⓒ noy
- Ⓓ nou

2.
- Ⓔ doun
- Ⓕ down
- Ⓖ doyn
- Ⓗ dowun

3.
- Ⓐ out
- Ⓑ ouwt
- Ⓒ owte
- Ⓓ owt

4.
- Ⓔ poynt
- Ⓕ poyint
- Ⓖ poyt
- Ⓗ point

5.
- Ⓐ joiy
- Ⓑ joy
- Ⓒ joi
- Ⓓ joye

6.
- Ⓔ house
- Ⓕ howse
- Ⓖ hous
- Ⓗ hows

7.
- Ⓐ coyn
- Ⓑ coyne
- Ⓒ coine
- Ⓓ coin

8.
- Ⓔ loude
- Ⓕ loud
- Ⓖ lowd
- Ⓗ lowde

9.
- Ⓐ broyn
- Ⓑ browne
- Ⓒ brown
- Ⓓ broun

10.
- Ⓔ couboy
- Ⓕ cowboi
- Ⓖ cowboy
- Ⓗ couboi

McGraw-Hill School Division

Words with /âr/*are*; /ôr/*or*, *ore*; and /îr/*ear*

Pretest Directions

Fold back your paper along the dotted line.
Use the blanks to write each word as it is said to you. When you finish the test, unfold the paper and correct any spelling mistakes. Practice those words for the Posttest.

To Parents,

Here are the results of your child's weekly spelling Pretest. You can help your child study for the Posttest by following these simple steps for each word on the word list:

1. Read the word to your child.
2. Have your child write the word, saying each letter as it is written.
3. Say each letter of the word as your child checks the spelling.
4. If a mistake has been made, have your child read each letter of the correctly spelled word aloud and then repeat steps 1–3.

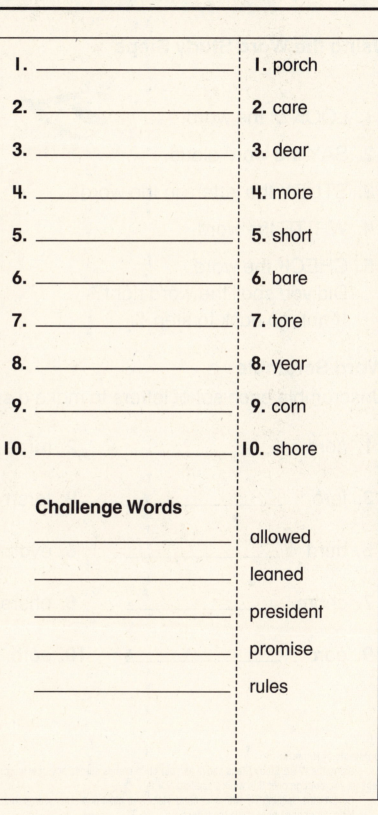

1. _____ 1. porch
2. _____ 2. care
3. _____ 3. dear
4. _____ 4. more
5. _____ 5. short
6. _____ 6. bare
7. _____ 7. tore
8. _____ 8. year
9. _____ 9. corn
10. _____ 10. shore

Challenge Words

_____ allowed
_____ leaned
_____ president
_____ promise
_____ rules

Words with /âr/ *are*; /ôr/ *or*, *ore*; and /îr/ *ear*

Using the Word Study Steps

1. LOOK at the word.

2. SAY the word aloud.

3. STUDY the letters in the word.

4. WRITE the word.

5. CHECK the word.
   Did you spell the word right?
   If not, go back to step 1.

> ### Spelling Tip
> Think of a word that rhymes with the new word. Rhyming words often have the same spelling pattern.
> Example:
> c + are = care
> b + are = bare

Word Scramble

Unscramble each set of letters to make a spelling word.

1. norc _____

2. rome _____

3. tero _____

4. torsh _____

5. aerd _____

6. eyar _____

7. chorp _____

8. ohsre _____

9. earc _____

10. earb _____

To Parents or Helpers:
   Using the Word Study Steps above as your child comes across any new words will help him or her spell well. Review the steps as you both go over this week's spelling words.
   Go over the Spelling Tip with your child. Help your child find other words that rhyme with the spelling words.
   Help your child unscramble the letters.

Words with /âr/*are*; /ôr/*or, ore*; and /îr/*ear*

porch	dear	short	tore	corn
care	more	bare	year	shore

Batter Up!

Fill the baseball bats with spelling words. Match each word with a spelling pattern.

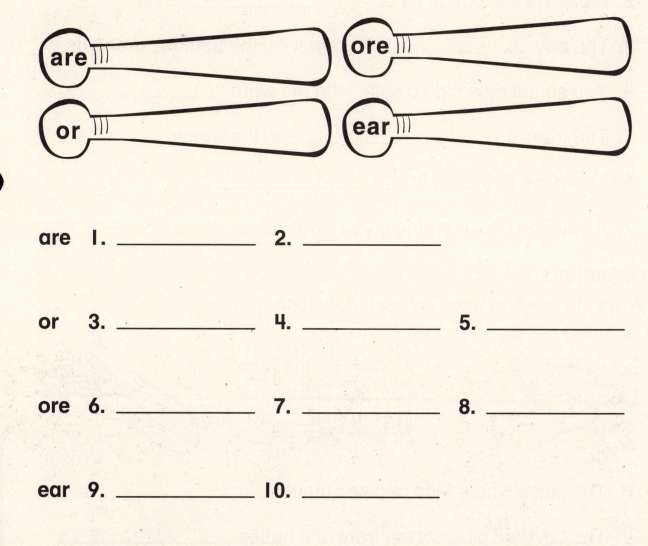

are 1. _____ 2. _____

or 3. _____ 4. _____ 5. _____

ore 6. _____ 7. _____ 8. _____

ear 9. _____ 10. _____

Words with /âr/*are*; /ôr/*or, ore*; and /îr/*ear*

porch	dear	short	tore	corn
care	more	bare	year	shore

Use a spelling word to complete each sentence.

1. It's important to take good _____ of your pet.

2. A giant is tall, but an elf is _____ .

3. The boy _____ the paper off the birthday presents.

4. You sometimes start a letter with the word "_____."

5. The trees are _____ in the winter.

6. There are 365 days in one _____ .

7. If you don't have enough, you want _____ .

Definitions

Write the spelling word for each definition.

8. The place where land and sea meet. _____

9. The covered place at the front of a house. _____

10. A yellow food that grows on a stalk. _____

Challenge Extension: Have children identify which of the
challenge words are either plural or past tense. Then
ask them to indicate the base words in those cases.

48

Book 2.1/Unit 2
Best Friends Club

10

McGraw-Hill School Division

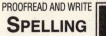

Words with /âr/*are*; /ôr/*or*, *ore*; and /îr/*ear*

Proofreading Activity

There are six spelling mistakes in the paragraph below. Circle each misspelled word. Write the words correctly on the lines below.

My best friend, Mark, and I played on my pourch. Then we went for a shorte walk to the shor. We had baer feet, so we had to take mor caer than we usually did. First we walked on our toes. Then, we walked on our heels. We had fun.

1. _____ 2. _____ 3. _____

4. _____ 5. _____ 6. _____

Writing Activity

Write a letter to a friend. Tell your friend about something you like to play. Use four of your spelling words. Circle the spelling words you use.

_____

_____

_____

_____

Words with /âr/*are*; /ôr/*or, ore*; and /îr/*ear*

Look at the words in each set. One word in each set is spelled correctly. Use a pencil to color in the circle in front of that word. Before you begin, look at the sample sets of words. Sample A has been done for you. Do Sample B by yourself. When you are sure you know what to do, you may go on with the rest of the page.

Sample A
- Ⓐ nite
- Ⓑ nighte
- Ⓒ nihgt
- ⬤ night

Sample B
- Ⓔ werd
- Ⓕ worde
- Ⓖ word
- Ⓗ werde

1.
- Ⓐ porch
- Ⓑ porsh
- Ⓒ porech
- Ⓓ porche

2.
- Ⓔ cear
- Ⓕ care
- Ⓖ caare
- Ⓗ caer

3.
- Ⓐ daer
- Ⓑ deare
- Ⓒ dear
- Ⓓ dere

4.
- Ⓔ mor
- Ⓕ morr
- Ⓖ moere
- Ⓗ more

5.
- Ⓐ shorte
- Ⓑ short
- Ⓒ shart
- Ⓓ sherte

6.
- Ⓔ toer
- Ⓕ torre
- Ⓖ tore
- Ⓗ torr

7.
- Ⓐ yeare
- Ⓑ yeer
- Ⓒ year
- Ⓓ yeere

8.
- Ⓔ cerne
- Ⓕ carn
- Ⓖ corne
- Ⓗ corn

9.
- Ⓐ baer
- Ⓑ baere
- Ⓒ baree
- Ⓓ bare

10.
- Ⓔ shore
- Ⓕ shorre
- Ⓖ shoer
- Ⓗ shor

Words with /är/ *ar*; /ûr/ *ir, er, ur*

Pretest Directions

Fold back your paper along the dotted line. Use the blanks to write each word as it is said to you. When you finish the test, unfold the paper, and correct any spelling mistakes. Practice those words for the Posttest.

To Parents,

Here are the results of your child's weekly spelling Pretest. You can help your child study for the Posttest by following these simple steps for each word on the word list:

1. Read the word to your child.

2. Have your child write the word, saying each letter as it is written.

3. Say each letter of the word as your child checks the spelling.

4. If a mistake has been made, have your child read each letter of the correctly spelled word aloud and then repeat steps 1–3.

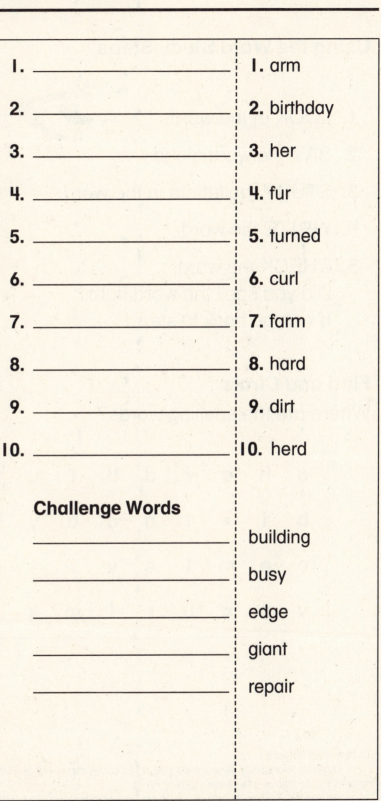

1. _____   **1.** arm

2. _____   **2.** birthday

3. _____   **3.** her

4. _____   **4.** fur

5. _____   **5.** turned

6. _____   **6.** curl

7. _____   **7.** farm

8. _____   **8.** hard

9. _____   **9.** dirt

10. _____   **10.** herd

Challenge Words

_____   building

_____   busy

_____   edge

_____   giant

_____   repair

Words with /är/ *ar*; /ûr/ *ir, er, ur*

Using the Word Study Steps

1. LOOK at the word.

2. SAY the word aloud.

3. STUDY the letters in the word.

4. WRITE the word.

5. CHECK the word.
   Did you spell the word right?
   If not, go back to step 1.

Spelling Tip

Word families have words that are related in meaning. Word families can help you write the new word.

Example:

turn, turned, turns, turning

Find and Circle

Where are the spelling words?

a	h	a	r	d	b	f	u	r	h	c	d	e
b	i	r	t	h	d	a	y	h	e	g	f	s
o	p	m	l	e	v	r	t	u	r	n	e	d
v	n	c	u	r	l	m	k	j	d	i	r	t

To Parents or Helpers:

Using the Word Study Steps above as your child comes across any new words will help him or her spell well. Review the steps as you both go over this week's spelling words.

Go over the Spelling Tip with your child. Ask your child for other words related to some of the spelling words.

Help your child find and circle the spelling words in the puzzle.

Words with /är/ *ar*; /ûr/ *ir*, *er*, *ur*

arm	her	turned	farm	dirt
birthday	fur	curl	hard	herd

Fill in the sand pails with spelling words. Match each word with a spelling pattern.

ar

1. _____

2. _____

3. _____

ir

4. _____

5. _____

er

6. _____

7. _____

ur

8. _____

9. _____

10. _____

Name _____ Date _____

PRACTICE AND EXTEND
SPELLING 54

Words with /är/ *ar*; /ûr/ *ir, er, ur*

arm	her	turned	farm	dirt
birthday	fur	curl	hard	herd

Write a spelling word to complete each sentence.

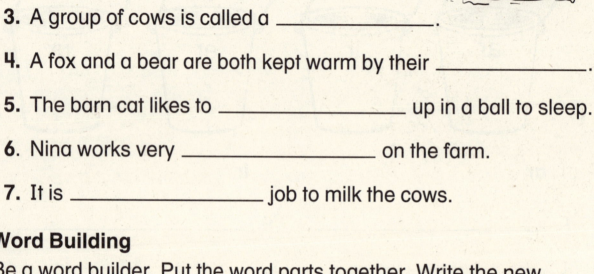

1. People raise animals on a _____.

2. Pigs like to roll in the _____.

3. A group of cows is called a _____.

4. A fox and a bear are both kept warm by their _____.

5. The barn cat likes to _____ up in a ball to sleep.

6. Nina works very _____ on the farm.

7. It is _____ job to milk the cows.

Word Building

Be a word builder. Put the word parts together. Write the new words you can make. Circle the part of the finished word that is a spelling word.

8. birth + day = _____

9. curl + ed = _____

10. turn + ed = _____

11. farm + house = _____

12. arm + chair = _____

Challenge Extension: Have children draw pictures and label them to illustrate the Challenge Words.

54

Book 2.1/Unit 2
Jamaica Tag-Along 12

Words with /är/ *ar*; /ûr/ *ir, er, ur*

Proofreading Activity

There are six spelling mistakes in the report below. Circle each misspelled word. Write the words correctly on the lines below.

I got a new pet snake for my berthday. I named hir Slinky because of the way she moves. Slinky does not have fer. She is smooth. Slinky likes to cerl around my erm. I really like my pet snake! I hope she likes living with me on the faarm.

1. _____   2. _____   3. _____

4. _____   5. _____   6. _____

Writing Activity

Write a short report about life on a farm. Use four of your spelling words. Circle the spelling words you use.

_____

_____

_____

_____

_____

_____

Words with /är/ *ar*; /ûr/ *ir, er, ur*

Look at the words in each set. One word in each set is spelled correctly. Use a pencil to color in the circle in front of that word. Before you begin, look at the sample sets of words. Sample A has been done for you. Do Sample B by yourself. When you are sure you know what to do, you may go on with the rest of the page.

Sample A
- (A) paint
- (B) paent
- (C) paynt
- (D) piant

Sample B
- (E) sleap
- (F) slepe
- (G) sleep
- (H) sleepe

1.
- (A) erm
- (B) arm
- (C) urm
- (D) irm

2.
- (E) barthday
- (F) berthday
- (G) birthday
- (H) burthday

3.
- (A) har
- (B) hir
- (C) hur
- (D) her

4.
- (E) fiar
- (F) fur
- (G) fer
- (H) fuir

5.
- (A) turned
- (B) tirmed
- (C) tarned
- (D) terned

6.
- (E) cerl
- (F) cerle
- (G) cirl
- (H) curl

7.
- (A) ferm
- (B) feirm
- (C) farm
- (D) furm

8.
- (E) hard
- (F) hird
- (G) harde
- (H) hurd

9.
- (A) dirt
- (B) dert
- (C) durt
- (D) deirt

10.
- (E) hird
- (F) herd
- (G) herde
- (H) hurd

Words from Science

Pretest Directions

Fold back your paper along the dotted line.
Use the blanks to write each word as it is said to you. When you finish the test, unfold the paper and correct any spelling mistakes. Practice those words for the Posttest.

To Parents,

Here are the results of your child's weekly spelling Pretest. You can help your child study for the Posttest by following these simple steps for each word on the word list:

1. Read the word to your child.

2. Have your child write the word, saying each letter as it is written.

3. Say each letter of the word as your child checks the spelling.

4. If a mistake has been made, have your child read each letter of the correctly spelled word aloud and then repeat steps 1–3.

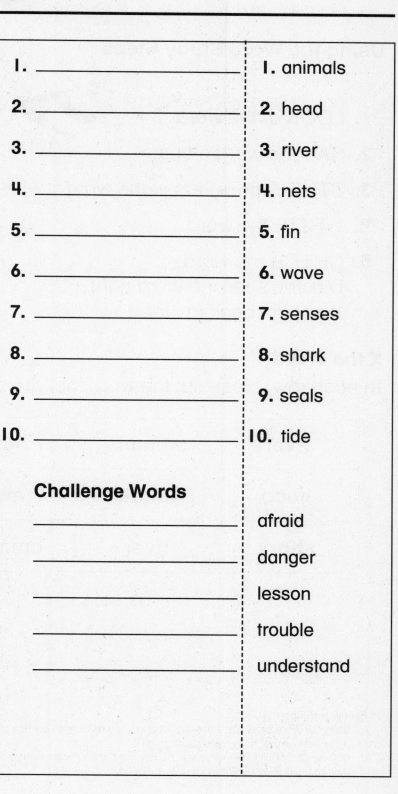

1. _____ 1. animals
2. _____ 2. head
3. _____ 3. river
4. _____ 4. nets
5. _____ 5. fin
6. _____ 6. wave
7. _____ 7. senses
8. _____ 8. shark
9. _____ 9. seals
10. _____ 10. tide

Challenge Words

_____ afraid

_____ danger

_____ lesson

_____ trouble

_____ understand

Words from Science

Using the Word Study Steps

1. LOOK at the word.

2. SAY the word aloud.

3. STUDY the letters in the word.

4. WRITE the word.

5. CHECK the word.
   Did you spell the word right?
   If not, go back to step 1.

Spelling Tip
Use the dictionary to look up spellings of words.

X the Word

In each row, cross out the word that does not belong.

river	animals	tide	wave
head	shark	nets	fin
shark	river	animals	seals

McGraw-Hill School Division

Words from Science

animals	river	fin	senses	seals
head	nets	wave	shark	tide

Write the spelling words that name one thing.

1. _____ 2. _____ 3. _____

4. _____ 5. _____ 6. _____

Write the spelling words that name more than one thing.

7. _____ 8. _____

9. _____ 10. _____

Words from Science

| animals | river | fin | senses | seals |
| head | nets | wave | shark | tide |

Use a spelling word to complete each sentence.

1. The best time to look for shells on the beach is at low _____.

2. A large _____ washed away my sand castle.

3. A shark has a special _____ on its back.

4. Mr. Johnson always wears a wool hat on his _____.

5. The workers feed all the _____ in the zoo twice a day.

6. My cat uses the _____ of sight and smell to hunt.

Word Meaning

Take off the **s** to make each spelling word singular.

1. animals – s = _____   2. nets – s = _____

3. senses – s = _____   4. seals – s = _____

Add **s** to make each spelling word plural.

5. head + s = _____   6. river + s = _____

7. fin + s = _____   8. wave + s = _____

9. shark + s = _____   10. tide + s = _____

McGraw-Hill School Division

Challenge Extension: Have students write a
sentence for each challenge word. Illustrate
sentences with a picture.

Words from Science

Proofreading Activity

There are five spelling mistakes in the paragraph below. Circle each misspelled word. Write the words correctly on the lines below.

Some animals like to eat fish. Some people like fish too. But anmals and people catch fish in different ways. A person might use a fishing pole to lift a fish from the rivr. Some people use nats to take fish from the ocean. Sels swim fast and catch fish in their mouths. A shrak uses his sharp teeth to gobble up large fish.

1. _____   2. _____

3. _____   4. _____

5. _____

Writing Activity

Write a story about things that live in the ocean. Use five spelling words in your story. Circle the spelling words you use.

_____

_____

_____

_____

_____

Words from Science

Look at the words in each set. One word in each set is spelled correctly. Use a pencil to color in the circle in front of that word. Before you begin, look at the sample sets of words. Sample A has been done for you. Do Sample B by yourself. When you are sure you know what to do, you may go on with the rest of the page.

Sample A
- Ⓐ fesh
- ⚫ fish
- Ⓒ fishe
- Ⓓ feesh

Sample B
- Ⓔ farn
- Ⓕ ferm
- Ⓖ farm
- Ⓗ farme

1. Ⓐ wav
   Ⓑ waev
   Ⓒ wave
   Ⓓ waev

2. Ⓔ haed
   Ⓕ hed
   Ⓖ hade
   Ⓗ head

3. Ⓐ animals
   Ⓑ aminals
   Ⓒ anmials
   Ⓓ anmails

4. Ⓔ rivr
   Ⓕ river
   Ⓖ rever
   Ⓗ revir

5. Ⓐ nes
   Ⓑ nets
   Ⓒ nts
   Ⓓ netes

6. Ⓔ fien
   Ⓕ fin
   Ⓖ fen
   Ⓗ fein

7. Ⓐ sesnes
   Ⓑ senses
   Ⓒ sences
   Ⓓ sens

8. Ⓔ saels
   Ⓕ seals
   Ⓖ siels
   Ⓗ seels

9. Ⓐ sharc
   Ⓑ shrak
   Ⓒ shark
   Ⓓ sharke

10. Ⓔ teid
    Ⓕ tide
    Ⓖ teed
    Ⓗ tid

McGraw-Hill School Division

Book 2.1/Unit 2 Review Test

Read each sentence. If an underlined word is spelled wrong, fill in the circle that goes with that word. If no word is spelled wrong, fill in the circle below NONE.
Read Sample A, and do Sample B.

A. Did you <u>hear</u> about the <u>blue</u> <u>mouse</u>?
             A   B   C

NONE
A. Ⓐ Ⓑ Ⓒ ●

B. My <u>toy</u> <u>horse</u> has soft <u>fur</u>.
       E   F   G

NONE
B. Ⓔ Ⓕ Ⓖ Ⓗ

1. The <u>sharke</u> will not come <u>down</u> to the <u>shore</u>.
       A   B   C

NONE
1. Ⓐ Ⓑ Ⓒ Ⓓ

2. The <u>curll</u> in <u>her</u> hair <u>blew</u> in the wind.
       E   F   G

NONE
2. Ⓔ Ⓕ Ⓖ Ⓗ

3. They have <u>animals</u> <u>down</u> on the <u>farm</u>.
            A   B   C

NONE
3. Ⓐ Ⓑ Ⓒ Ⓓ

4. Our <u>schole</u> has a <u>porch</u> near our <u>room</u>.
       E   F   G

NONE
4. Ⓔ Ⓕ Ⓖ Ⓗ

5. The zookeeper <u>takes</u> good <u>cayre</u> of her <u>seals</u>.
              A   B   C

NONE
5. Ⓐ Ⓑ Ⓒ Ⓓ

6. They jump for <u>joye</u> to see the <u>farm</u> <u>animals</u>.
             E   F G

NONE
6. Ⓔ Ⓕ Ⓖ Ⓗ

7. There is a <u>clue</u> <u>down</u> in my <u>rume</u>.
           A B   C

NONE
7. Ⓐ Ⓑ Ⓒ Ⓓ

8. This <u>year</u> we can feed the <u>seales</u> at the <u>shore</u>.
       E   F   G

NONE
8. Ⓔ Ⓕ Ⓖ Ⓗ

9. The <u>wind</u> <u>blue</u> a coin across the <u>porch</u>.
       A   B   C

NONE
9. Ⓐ Ⓑ Ⓒ Ⓓ

Go on

McGraw-Hill School Division

Book 2.1/Unit 2 Review Test

10. This <u>yere</u> I am in the new <u>school</u> <u>room</u>.
      E   F   G

10. Ⓔ Ⓕ Ⓖ Ⓗ NONE

11. The <u>animals</u> swam <u>down</u> the <u>rivver</u>.
         A   B   C

11. Ⓐ Ⓑ Ⓒ Ⓓ NONE

12. The <u>clue</u> is <u>down</u> at the <u>shoore</u>.
        E   F   G

12. Ⓔ Ⓕ Ⓖ Ⓗ NONE

13. This <u>coin</u> is in <u>herr</u> <u>room</u>.
        A   B   C

13. Ⓐ Ⓑ Ⓒ Ⓓ NONE

14. The <u>seels</u> are on the <u>house</u> <u>porch</u>.
      E   F   G

14. Ⓔ Ⓕ Ⓖ Ⓗ NONE

15. He <u>gave</u> her a <u>coine</u> for her <u>birthday</u>.
      A   B   C

15. Ⓐ Ⓑ Ⓒ Ⓓ NONE

16. I <u>care</u> for the <u>animales</u> on the <u>farm</u>.
    E   F   G

16. Ⓔ Ⓕ Ⓖ Ⓗ NONE

17. <u>Her</u> mom's <u>birthday</u> is later this <u>year</u>.
    A   B   C

17. Ⓐ Ⓑ Ⓒ Ⓓ NONE

18. I sat on the <u>porche</u> <u>swing</u> by the <u>shore</u>.
            E   F   G

18. Ⓔ Ⓕ Ⓖ Ⓗ NONE

19. The leaf <u>blew</u> <u>downe</u> the <u>river</u>.
          A   B   C

19. Ⓐ Ⓑ Ⓒ Ⓓ NONE

20. <u>Her</u> <u>animals</u> are never in the <u>house</u>.
    E   F   G

20. Ⓔ Ⓕ Ⓖ Ⓗ NONE

Book 2.1/Unit 2
Unit Review Test /20

Words with Silent Letters

Pretest Directions

Fold back the paper along the dotted line. Use the blanks to write each word as it is read aloud. When you finish the test, unfold the paper. Correct any spelling mistakes. Practice the words you missed for the Posttest.

To Parents,

Here are the results of your child's weekly spelling Pretest. You can help your child study for the Posttest by following these simple steps for each word on the list:

1. Read the word to your child.

2. Have your child write the word, saying each letter as it is written.

3. Say each letter of the word as your child checks the spelling.

4. If a mistake has been made, have your child read each letter of the correctly spelled word aloud, and then repeat steps 1–3.

1. _____ 1. high

2. _____ 2. know

3. _____ 3. half

4. _____ 4. wrote

5. _____ 5. thumb

6. _____ 6. lamb

7. _____ 7. knee

8. _____ 8. right

9. _____ 9. knot

10. _____ 10. write

Challenge Words

_____ decided

_____ important

_____ library

_____ planet

_____ proud

Words with Silent Letters

Using the Word Study Steps

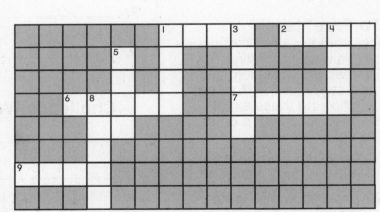

1. LOOK at the word.
2. SAY the word aloud.
3. STUDY the letters in the word.
4. WRITE the word.
5. CHECK the word.
   Did you spell the word right?
   If not, go back to step 1.

Spelling Tip
Make up clues to help you remember the spelling.
Example:
Be gentle with a lam**b**.
(Lamb ends with a **b**.)

Crossword Puzzle

Write the spelling word that best matches each clue. Put the spelling words in the boxes that start with the same number.

CROSSWORD CLUES

ACROSS
1. understand
2. two of these make a whole
6. put words on paper yesterday
7. special finger
9. not low

DOWN
1. where your leg bends
3. what an author does
4. a baby sheep
5. your laces are tied with this
8. correct

To Parents or Helpers:
Using the Word Study Steps above as your child comes across any new words will help him or her spell well. Review the steps as you both go over this week's spelling words.
Go over the Spelling Tip with your child. Help him or her make up clues for other words, such as thumb or right.
Help your child solve the crossword puzzle.

Words with Silent Letters

high	half	thumb	knee	knot
know	wrote	lamb	right	write

Look at the spelling words in the box.
Each spelling word has a silent letter. Match each word to a spelling pattern. Write the spelling words on the lines below.

Silent l

1. _____

Silent b

2. _____

3. _____

Silent k

4. _____

5. _____

6. _____

Silent w

7. _____

8. _____

Silent gh

9. _____

10. _____

McGraw-Hill School Division

Words with Silent Letters

high	half	thumb	knee	knot
know	wrote	lamb	right	write

Write a spelling word to complete each sentence.

1. Help me untie the _____.

2. I will give you _____ of my apple.

3. A baby sheep is called a _____.

4. Do you _____ the answer?

5. Your _____ is on your hand.

6. You can bend your leg at the _____.

7. The opposite of **left** is _____.

8. The opposite of **low** is _____.

9. I will _____ a letter to my mom.

10. I _____ a letter to my brother.

Word Builder

Be a word builder. Add the ending *-ed* to the word. First, double the final consonant.

knot + t + ed = _____

Challenge Extension: Have children complete this sentence: I think the library is important because _____.

Book 2.1/Unit 3
Arthur Writes a Story

10

McGraw-Hill School Division

Words with Silent Letters

Proofreading Activity

There are six spelling mistakes in the story below. Circle each misspelled word. Write the words correctly on the lines below.

One day a first grader in my school had a kot in his shoelace. He was haf my size. He asked me to help him. I didn't noe the rit way to get the knot out. I tried pulling it, but that didn't work. I took his shoe off and set it on my nee. Then I could hold the shoe with my thum and undo the knot with my fingers. Afterwards, his mother wrote my mother a note saying that I was a great kid.

1. _____ 2. _____ 3. _____

4. _____ 5. _____ 6. _____

Writing Activity

Write about a time when someone helped you. Use four of your spelling words. Circle the spelling words you use.

_____

_____

_____

_____

_____

Words with Silent Letters

Look at the words in each set. One word in each set is spelled right. Use a pencil to color in the circle in front of that word. Before you begin, look at the sample sets of words. Sample A has been done for you. Do Sample B by yourself. When you are sure you know what to do, you may go on with the rest of the page.

Sample A
- Ⓐ sihg
- Ⓑ siep
- Ⓒ sigh ●
- Ⓓ sighe

Sample B
- Ⓔ currl
- Ⓕ curl
- Ⓖ kurl
- Ⓗ curle

1.
- Ⓐ hih
- Ⓑ hihg
- Ⓒ high
- Ⓓ hihgt

2.
- Ⓔ kno
- Ⓕ know
- Ⓖ khow
- Ⓗ noo

3.
- Ⓐ haf
- Ⓑ half
- Ⓒ haff
- Ⓓ havf

4.
- Ⓔ wote
- Ⓕ roate
- Ⓖ whote
- Ⓗ wrote

5.
- Ⓐ thumb
- Ⓑ thum
- Ⓒ tfum
- Ⓓ thumgh

6.
- Ⓔ lamb
- Ⓕ lamm
- Ⓖ lamme
- Ⓗ labm

7.
- Ⓐ kne
- Ⓑ nea
- Ⓒ nei
- Ⓓ knee

8.
- Ⓔ kot
- Ⓕ knoght
- Ⓖ knot
- Ⓗ khot

9.
- Ⓐ riyte
- Ⓑ right
- Ⓒ riht
- Ⓓ ritgh

10.
- Ⓔ wite
- Ⓕ write
- Ⓖ rwite
- Ⓗ wrrite

McGraw-Hill School Division

Book 2.1/Unit 3
Arthur Writes a Story
10

Words ending with /ər/*er*

Pretest Directions

Fold back the paper along the dotted line. Use the blanks to write each word as it is read aloud. When you finish the test, unfold the paper. Correct any spelling mistakes. Practice the words you missed for the Posttest.

To Parents,

Here are the results of your child's weekly spelling Pretest. You can help your child study for the Posttest by following these simple steps for each word on the list:

1. Read the word to your child.

2. Have your child write the word, saying each letter as it is written.

3. Say each letter of the word as your child checks the spelling.

4. If a mistake has been made, have your child read each letter of the correctly spelled word aloud, and then repeat steps 1–3.

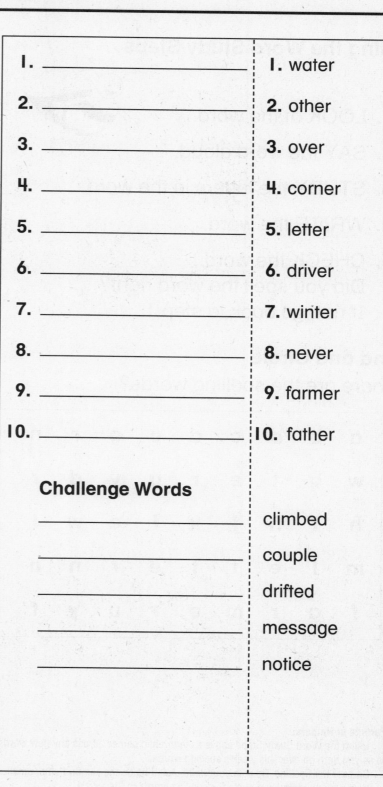

1. _____	1. water
2. _____	2. other
3. _____	3. over
4. _____	4. corner
5. _____	5. letter
6. _____	6. driver
7. _____	7. winter
8. _____	8. never
9. _____	9. farmer
10. _____	10. father

Challenge Words

_____	climbed
_____	couple
_____	drifted
_____	message
_____	notice

Words ending with /ər/*er*

Using the Word Study Steps

1. LOOK at the word.

2. SAY the word aloud.

3. STUDY the letters in the word.

4. WRITE the word.

5. CHECK the word.
   Did you spell the word right?
   If not, go back to step 1.

Spelling Tip

Look for a smaller word in a new word to help you write the new word.

win + ter = winter

Find and Circle

Where are the spelling words?

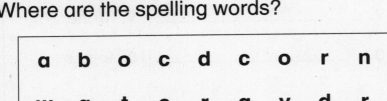

a	b	o	c	d	c	o	r	n	e	r	e	f	n
w	a	t	e	r	g	v	d	r	i	v	e	r	e
h	i	h	j	k	l	e	w	i	n	t	e	r	v
m	l	e	t	t	e	r	n	n	x	p	r	t	e
f	a	r	m	e	r	u	y	f	a	t	h	e	r

To Parents or Helpers:
    Using the Word Study Steps above as your child comes across any new words will help him or her spell well. Review the steps as you both go over this week's spelling words.
    Go over the Spelling Tip with your child. Ask if he or she can find other smaller words in new words.
    Help your child find and circle the spelling words in the puzzle.

Book 2.1/Unit 3
Best Wishes, Ed 10

McGraw-Hill School Division

Name _____ Date _____

Words ending with /ər/*er*

water	over	letter	winter	farmer
other	corner	driver	never	father

Fill the icebergs with spelling words that follow the spelling patterns.

words ending with *ther*

1. _____
2. _____

words ending with *ter*

3. _____
4. _____
5. _____

words ending with *ver*

6. _____
7. _____
8. _____

words ending with *er*

9. _____
10. _____

Words ending with /ər/er

water	over	letter	winter	farmer
other	corner	driver	never	father

Use spelling words to complete each sentence.

1. The opposite of **always** is _____.

2. _____ is my favorite season because I like to ice skate.

3. Another word for **dad** is _____.

4. The opposite of **under** is _____.

5. I wrote a _____ to my friend.

6. Meet me at the _____ of Main Street and Oak Avenue.

7. Do you want this one or the _____ one?

8. Do you want a drink of _____?

9. A _____ grows food.

10. The bus _____ takes my money.

Challenge Extension: Have children pretend they are shipwrecked. They may use challenge words to write a message to put in a bottle.

Book 2.1/Unit 3
Best Wishes, Ed
10

McGraw-Hill School Division

Words ending with /ər/*er*

Read the sentences. There is one spelling mistake in each sentence. Circle the mistake. Write the correct word on the line.

1. Tom, please send me a leter.

2. Matt, why don't you swim ovir here today?

3. Who wants to go fishing with Sue and her fathar?

4. There will be a wintor party for all of the penguins on Saturday night.

5. Mike is looking for othur penguins to help build a snowman.

6. Please meet me at the cornir.

1. _____ **2.** _____ **3.** _____

4. _____ **5.** _____ **6.** _____

Writing Activity

Pretend that you are a farmer. Write a letter to your city friend and invite him to visit you. Tell him what he will see at your farm. Use four of your spelling words. Circle the spelling words you use.

_____

_____

_____

_____

McGraw-Hill School Division

Words ending with /ər/*er*

Look at the words in each set. One word in each set is spelled right. Use a pencil to color in the circle in front of that word. Before you begin, look at the sample sets of words. Sample A has been done for you. Do Sample B by yourself. When you are sure you know what to do, you may go on with the rest of the page.

Sample A
- Ⓐ paeper
- Ⓑ parper
- Ⓒ paper
- Ⓓ peper

Sample B
- Ⓔ half
- Ⓕ haf
- Ⓖ halfe
- Ⓗ haffe

1.
- Ⓐ watir
- Ⓑ wator
- Ⓒ water
- Ⓓ watar

2.
- Ⓔ other
- Ⓕ othir
- Ⓖ othar
- Ⓗ othur

3.
- Ⓐ ovir
- Ⓑ ovar
- Ⓒ over
- Ⓓ ovur

4.
- Ⓔ cornar
- Ⓕ corner
- Ⓖ cornir
- Ⓗ cornure

5.
- Ⓐ leter
- Ⓑ lettir
- Ⓒ lettor
- Ⓓ letter

6.
- Ⓔ drivor
- Ⓕ drivur
- Ⓖ driver
- Ⓗ drivar

7.
- Ⓐ winter
- Ⓑ wintor
- Ⓒ wintere
- Ⓓ wintur

8.
- Ⓔ nevur
- Ⓕ nevir
- Ⓖ never
- Ⓗ nevar

9.
- Ⓐ farmir
- Ⓑ farmer
- Ⓒ farmor
- Ⓓ farmar

10.
- Ⓔ fathur
- Ⓕ fathre
- Ⓖ fathir
- Ⓗ father

McGraw-Hill School Division

Words with Short *e*: *ea*

Pretest Directions

Fold back the paper along the dotted line. Use the blanks to write each word as it is read aloud. When you finish the test, unfold the paper. Correct any spelling mistakes. Practice the words you missed for the Posttest.

To Parents,

Here are the results of your child's weekly spelling Pretest. You can help your child study for the Posttest by following these simple steps for each word on the list:

1. Read the word to your child.

2. Have your child write the word, saying each letter as it is written.

3. Say each letter of the word as your child checks the spelling.

4. If a mistake has been made, have your child read each letter of the correctly spelled word aloud, and then repeat steps 1–3.

1. _____	**1.** leather
2. _____	**2.** bread
3. _____	**3.** weather
4. _____	**4.** spread
5. _____	**5.** breakfast
6. _____	**6.** ready
7. _____	**7.** meant
8. _____	**8.** feather
9. _____	**9.** instead
10. _____	**10.** meadow

Challenge Words

_____	arrive
_____	early
_____	finish
_____	record
_____	success

Words with Short *e: ea*

Using the Word Study Steps

1. LOOK at the word.

2. SAY the word aloud.

3. STUDY the letters in the word.

4. WRITE the word.

5. CHECK the word.
   Did you spell the word right?
   If not, go back to step 1.

Spelling Tip

Short vowel sounds are usually spelled with one vowel. But sometimes they are spelled with two vowels. Think of ways to remember the spelling of short **e** in these words.
Example:
I am r**ea**dy for br**ea**d.

Find and Circle

Where are the spelling words?

b	r	e	a	k	f	a	s	t	a	c	d	g	o	b
l	e	a	t	h	e	r	m	w	e	a	t	h	e	r
k	a	f	e	a	t	h	e	r	m	e	a	n	t	e
x	d	f	m	e	a	d	o	w	u	q	j	s	p	a
r	y	i	n	s	t	e	a	d	s	p	r	e	a	d

To Parents or Helpers:
Using the Word Study Steps above as your child comes across any new words will help him or her spell well. Review the steps as you both go over this week's spelling words.
Go over the Spelling Tip with your child. Ask if he or she knows other words with short vowels spelled with two vowels.
Help your child find and circle the spelling words in the puzzle.

Name _____ Date _____

Words with Short *e*: *ea*

ready	leather	meant	instead	meadow
spread	breakfast	weather	bread	feather

It's in the Mail!

Look at the spelling words in the box.

Say each spelling word. Tap the number of syllables in each word. Write the spelling words that have one syllable and two syllables in the correct Pony Express bags below.

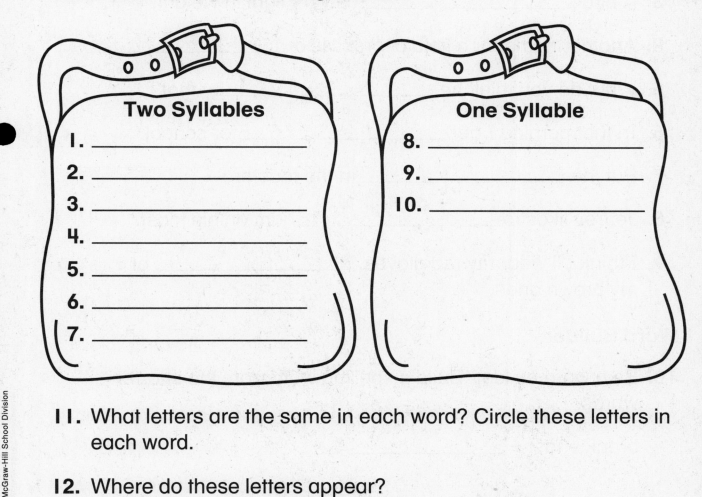

Two Syllables

1. _____
2. _____
3. _____
4. _____
5. _____
6. _____
7. _____

One Syllable

8. _____
9. _____
10. _____

11. What letters are the same in each word? Circle these letters in each word.

12. Where do these letters appear?

    at the beginning   in the middle   at the end

Words with Short *e*: *ea*

ready	leather	meant	instead	meadow
spread	breakfast	weather	bread	feather

Write a spelling word to complete each sentence.

1. Shoes and belts are made of _____.

2. The _____ can be hot or cold, rainy or clear.

3. A bird's _____ is very light in weight.

4. Another name for a field of grass is a _____.

5. What do you think he _____ by that?

6. In the morning I get _____ for school.

7. Put the _____ in the toaster.

8. Jeffrey likes to _____ jam on his toast.

9. I think I'll wear my red gloves _____ of my brown ones.

Word Builder

10. Be a word builder. Build a spelling word from the shorter words.

    break + fast = _____

Challenge Extension: Have children write sentences giving advice about the best way to win a race.

McGraw-Hill School Division

Words with Short *e*: *ea*

Proofreading Activity

There are six spelling mistakes in the journal below. Circle each misspelled word. Write the words correctly on the lines below.

Today was my first day as a Pony Express rider. In the morning the wether was beautiful. I had some bred for brekfst. I was too excited to eat anything else. I was reddy when the other rider got to my station. I put my lether bags across the saddle. Then, I jumped on my horse and was off! At first I rode along a river. After that I rode through a medow full of pretty wildflowers. Being a Pony Express rider is the best job I ever had!

I. _____ 2. _____ 3. _____

4. _____ 5. _____ 6. _____

Writing Activity

Pretend you are the Pony Express rider. Write about an exciting day you had. Use four of your spelling words. Circle the words you use.

_____

_____

_____

_____

_____

Words with Short *e*: *ea*

Look at the words in each set. One word in each set is spelled correctly. Use a pencil to color in the circle in front of that word. Before you begin, look at the sample sets of words. Sample A has been done for you. Do Sample B by yourself. When you are sure you know what to do, you may go on with the rest of the page.

Sample A
- Ⓐ watur
- ⬤Ⓑ water
- Ⓒ watir
- Ⓓ wator

Sample B
- Ⓔ yellow
- Ⓕ yello
- Ⓖ yellar
- Ⓗ yellur

1.
- Ⓐ leether
- Ⓑ laether
- Ⓒ leather
- Ⓓ layther

2.
- Ⓔ brede
- Ⓕ braed
- Ⓖ bread
- Ⓗ brid

3.
- Ⓐ weather
- Ⓑ wuther
- Ⓒ wather
- Ⓓ wether

4.
- Ⓔ spraed
- Ⓕ sprede
- Ⓖ spreed
- Ⓗ spread

5.
- Ⓐ bredfast
- Ⓑ breakfast
- Ⓒ brakfast
- Ⓓ brekfast

6.
- Ⓔ rady
- Ⓕ ready
- Ⓖ redy
- Ⓗ reddy

7.
- Ⓐ ment
- Ⓑ mante
- Ⓒ mente
- Ⓓ meant

8.
- Ⓔ feather
- Ⓕ faether
- Ⓖ fether
- Ⓗ feither

9.
- Ⓐ instaed
- Ⓑ instead
- Ⓒ instede
- Ⓓ instade

10.
- Ⓔ medow
- Ⓕ maedow
- Ⓖ meadow
- Ⓗ medou

Words with Long *e*: *y, ey*

Pretest Directions

Fold back the paper along the dotted line. Use the blanks to write each word as it is read aloud. When you finish the test, unfold the paper. Correct any spelling mistakes. Practice the words you missed for the Posttest.

To Parents,

Here are the results of your child's weekly spelling Pretest. You can help your child study for the Posttest by following these simple steps for each word on the list:

1. Read the word to your child.

2. Have your child write the word, saying each letter as it is written.

3. Say each letter of the word as your child checks the spelling.

4. If a mistake has been made, have your child read each letter of the correctly spelled word aloud, and then repeat steps 1–3.

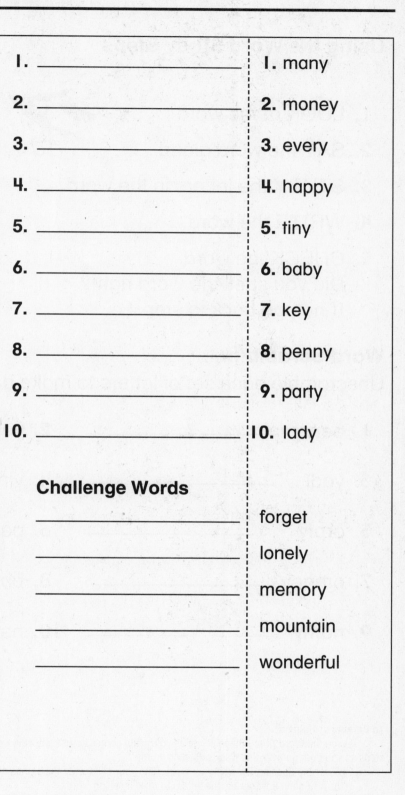

1. _____ 1. many

2. _____ 2. money

3. _____ 3. every

4. _____ 4. happy

5. _____ 5. tiny

6. _____ 6. baby

7. _____ 7. key

8. _____ 8. penny

9. _____ 9. party

10. _____ 10. lady

Challenge Words

_____ forget

_____ lonely

_____ memory

_____ mountain

_____ wonderful

McGraw-Hill School Division

Words with Long *e*: *y, ey*

Using the Word Study Steps

1. LOOK at the word.

2. SAY the word aloud.

3. STUDY the letters in the word.

4. WRITE the word.

5. CHECK the word.
   Did you spell the word right?
   If not, go back to step 1.

Spelling Tip

When a base word ends with a vowel followed by **y**, do not change the ending when adding suffixes or endings.

key + **s** = key**s**

Word Scramble

Unscramble each set of letters to make a spelling word.

1. eervy _____

2. yek _____

3. yadl _____

4. yint _____

5. arpty _____

6. paphy _____

7. omney _____

8. bbay _____

9. namy _____

10. nepny _____

To Parents or Helpers:
   Using the Word Study Steps above as your child comes across any new words will help him or her spell well. Review the steps as you both go over this week's spelling words.
   Go over the Spelling Tip with your child. Help your child write the plurals of words that end with a vowel followed by y.
   Help your child unscramble the letters to make spelling words.

McGraw-Hill School Division

Words with Long *e*: *y, ey*

Look at the words in the box. Write the spelling words that have each spelling pattern.

many	every	tiny	key	party
money	happy	baby	penny	lady

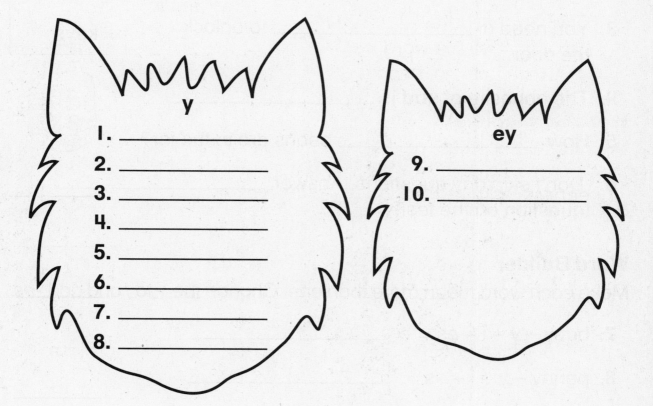

y

1. _____
2. _____
3. _____
4. _____
5. _____
6. _____
7. _____
8. _____

ey

9. _____
10. _____

Words with Long *e*: *y, ey*

many	every	tiny	key	party
money	happy	baby	penny	lady

Use a spelling word to complete each sentence.

1. People use _____ to buy things.

2. Something very small is _____.

3. You need a _____ to unlock the door.

4. The opposite of **sad** is _____.

5. How _____ beans are in the jar?

6. Don't skip any questions. Answer _____ question on the test.

Word Builder

Make each word mean more than one. Change the *y* to *i* and add *-es*.

7. baby − y + i + es = _____

8. penny − y + i + es = _____

9. party − y + i + es = _____

10. lady − y + i + es = _____

Challenge Extension: Have children write and illustrate an advertisement for a vacation spot in the mountains.

86

Book 2.1/Unit 3
Nine-in-One, Grr! Grr! 10

McGraw-Hill School Division

Words with Long *e*: *y*, *ey*

Proofreading Activity

There are six spelling mistakes in this report. Circle each misspelled word. Write the words correctly on the lines below.

There were meny tigers in the world. Then people began to live where the tigers live. Tigers had less space to live. Now there are few tigers left. Someday soon everey tiger in the world may be gone! Some people give mony to save the tigers. Other people work to save the tigers. People who work in zoos take care of babey tigers. The tiney tigers are safe and hapy there. Everyone can play a part in helping to save the tigers.

1. _____ 2. _____ 3. _____

4. _____ 5. _____ 6. _____

Writing Activity

Pretend you found a magic key. Write a story about the key. Use four of your spelling words. Circle the words you use.

_____

_____

_____

_____

_____

McGraw-Hill School Division

Words with Long *e*: *y*, *ey*

Look at the words in each set. One word in each set is spelled right. Use a pencil to color in the circle in front of that word. Before you begin, look at the sample sets of words. Sample A has been done for you. Do Sample B by yourself. When you are sure you know what to do, you may go on with the rest of the page.

Sample A
- Ⓐ candy
- Ⓑ candie
- Ⓒ candee
- Ⓓ candey

Sample B
- Ⓔ reidy
- Ⓕ raedy
- Ⓖ ready
- Ⓗ readey

1.
- Ⓐ maney
- Ⓑ many
- Ⓒ meny
- Ⓓ meney

2.
- Ⓔ mony
- Ⓕ moeny
- Ⓖ money
- Ⓗ monie

3.
- Ⓐ evere
- Ⓑ everi
- Ⓒ every
- Ⓓ evrey

4.
- Ⓔ happi
- Ⓕ happy
- Ⓖ hapy
- Ⓗ hapi

5.
- Ⓐ tiny
- Ⓑ tinie
- Ⓒ tieny
- Ⓓ tiney

6.
- Ⓔ baby
- Ⓕ babie
- Ⓖ babee
- Ⓗ babey

7.
- Ⓐ kee
- Ⓑ key
- Ⓒ kie
- Ⓓ keye

8.
- Ⓔ pennie
- Ⓕ penee
- Ⓖ peney
- Ⓗ penny

9.
- Ⓐ partee
- Ⓑ partie
- Ⓒ partey
- Ⓓ party

10.
- Ⓔ ladie
- Ⓕ ladee
- Ⓖ lady
- Ⓗ ladey

McGraw-Hill School Division

Words from Math

Pretest Directions

Fold back the paper along the dotted line. Use the blanks to write each word as it is read aloud. When you finish the test, unfold the paper. Correct any spelling mistakes. Practice the words you missed for the Posttest.

To Parents,

Here are the results of your child's weekly spelling Pretest. You can help your child study for the Posttest by following these simple steps for each word on the list:

1. Read the word to your child.

2. Have your child write the word, saying each letter as it is written.

3. Say each letter of the word as your child checks the spelling.

4. If a mistake has been made, have your child read each letter of the correctly spelled word aloud, and then repeat steps 1–3.

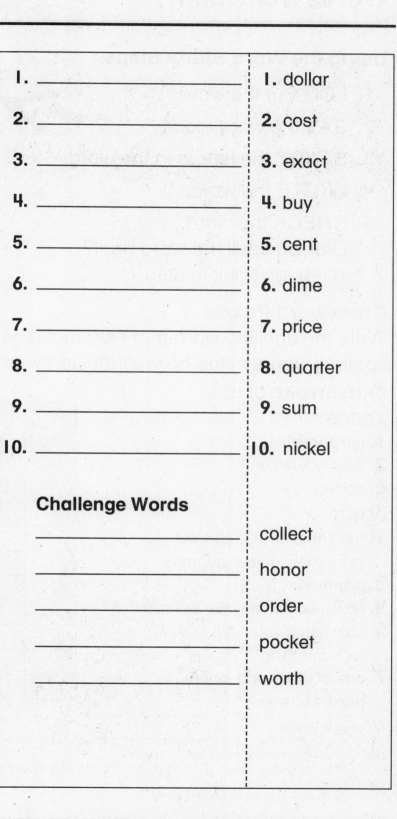

1. _____   **1.** dollar

2. _____   **2.** cost

3. _____   **3.** exact

4. _____   **4.** buy

5. _____   **5.** cent

6. _____   **6.** dime

7. _____   **7.** price

8. _____   **8.** quarter

9. _____   **9.** sum

10. _____   **10.** nickel

Challenge Words

_____   collect

_____   honor

_____   order

_____   pocket

_____   worth

McGraw-Hill School Division

Words from Math

Using the Word Study Steps

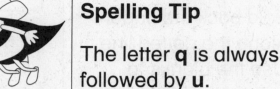

1. LOOK at the word.
2. SAY the word aloud.
3. STUDY the letters in the word.
4. WRITE the word.
5. CHECK the word.
   Did you spell the word right?
   If not, go back to step 1.

> **Spelling Tip**
>
> The letter **q** is always followed by **u**.
> Example:
>
> **qu**arter

Crossword Puzzle

Write the spelling word that best matches each clue. Put the spelling words in the boxes that start with the same number.

CROSSWORD CLUES

ACROSS

1. ten cents
2. twenty-five cents
6. correct

DOWN

1. the same as 100 pennies, ten dimes, or four quarters
3. pay money for
4. how much money the seller wants
5. how much you have to pay for something
7. one of these and four more makes a nickel

To Parents or Helpers:
Using the Word Study Steps above as your child comes across any new words will help him or her spell well. Review the steps as you both go over this week's spelling words.
Go over the Spelling Tip with your child. Ask him or her for other words that contain the letter **q**. Help him or her spell these words correctly.
Help your child solve the crossword puzzle.

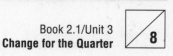

Words from Math

dollar	exact	cent	price	sum
cost	buy	dime	quarter	nickel

Look at the words in the box. Write the spelling words with one syllable.

1. _____ 2. _____ 3. _____

4. _____ 5. _____ 6. _____

Write the spelling words with two syllables.

7. _____ 8. _____

9. _____ 10. _____

Find and circle eight spelling words in the puzzle. Some of the words in the puzzle go across. Some of the words go down.

p	b	u	y	t	v	s	e	z	a
s	r	o	e	h	m	n	x	y	g
u	o	t	d	o	l	l	a	r	g
t	p	v	l	u	m	v	c	e	c
r	r	x	u	d	o	s	t	v	o
d	i	m	e	d	o	l	a	n	s
s	c	a	n	i	c	k	e	l	t
n	e	x	q	u	a	r	t	e	r

Words from Math

dollar	exact	cent	price	sum
cost	buy	dime	quarter	nickel

Write the spelling words that are names for money.

1. _____   2. _____

3. _____   4. _____

5. _____

Write the spelling words besides **buy** that tell about buying things.

6. _____   7. _____

Write the spelling word that means "correct" to complete the sentence.

8. The man in the store gave me _____ change for a dollar.

Answer these questions with a spelling word. Write the word on the line.

9. Which is more money: a dollar or a quarter?
   _____

10. Which is less money: a dime or a cent? _____

11. A dollar is the same as 4 _____.

12. A dollar is the same as 10 _____.

Challenge Extension: Have children make a pocket out of paper. Ask them to write challenge words on slips of paper and put them in the pocket.

McGraw-Hill School Division

Words from Math

Proofreading Activity

There are six spelling mistakes in the story below. Circle each misspelled word. Write the words correctly on the lines below.

Carlos wanted a yo-yo. He saw one he liked at the store. The tag showed the eggzact price: $1.25. Carlos looked in his pocket. He had one doller and one qarter. He felt really happy that he could buy the yo-yo.

Carlos gave the money to the saleslady.

She smiled at him and said, "This costz one dollar and thirty-five sents."

Carlos was surprised. "I just have this much," he said.

"Sorry," said the lady. "You must give me another diem. You forgot the tax."

Carlos was lucky. He found the coin in another pocket and bought the yo-yo.

1. _____ 2. _____ 3. _____

4. _____ 5. _____ 6. _____

Writing Activity

Write about buying something. Tell how much it cost. Tell how many dollars and cents you paid. Use four of your spelling words. Circle the words you use.

_____

_____

_____

_____

Words from Math

Look at the words in each set. One word in each set is spelled right. Use a pencil to color in the circle in front of that word. Before you begin, look at the sample sets of words. Sample A has been done for you. Do Sample B by yourself. When you are sure you know what to do, you may go on with the rest of the page.

Sample A
- (A) one
- (B) wun
- (C) onne

Sample B
- (D) penny
- (E) peny
- (F) pennie

1.
- (A) dolar
- (B) dollar
- (C) doller

2.
- (D) kost
- (E) cawst
- (F) cost

3.
- (A) eggzact
- (B) eggsact
- (C) exact

4.
- (D) buy
- (E) bi
- (F) biy

5.
- (A) sentt
- (B) cent
- (C) scente

6.
- (D) diem
- (E) dym
- (F) dime

7.
- (A) prise
- (B) price
- (C) pris

8.
- (D) quarter
- (E) qarter
- (F) corter

9.
- (A) sume
- (B) som
- (C) sum

10.
- (D) nickle
- (E) nickel
- (F) nikel

McGraw-Hill School Division

Book 2.1/Unit 3 Review Test

Read each sentence. If an underlined word is spelled wrong, fill in the circle that goes with that word. If no word is spelled wrong, fill in the circle below NONE.
Read Sample A, and do Sample B.

A. My <u>sister</u> hurt her <u>thum</u> at the <u>park</u>.
     A   B   C

NONE
A. Ⓐ ⬤ Ⓒ Ⓓ

B. The <u>baby</u> likes the <u>bright</u> <u>light</u>.
      E   F   G

NONE
B. Ⓔ Ⓕ Ⓖ Ⓗ

1. I got a <u>letter</u> with a <u>sent</u> and a <u>quarter</u> in it.
          A   B   C

NONE
1. Ⓐ Ⓑ Ⓒ Ⓓ

2. I <u>rote</u> a <u>letter</u> to the <u>farmer</u>.
    E   F   G

NONE
2. Ⓔ Ⓕ Ⓖ Ⓗ

3. We <u>spred</u> the <u>bread</u> with jam <u>instead</u>.
      A   B   C

NONE
3. Ⓐ Ⓑ Ⓒ Ⓓ

4. I hurt my <u>other</u> <u>nee</u> jumping <u>over</u> a ball.
          E   F   G

NONE
4. Ⓔ Ⓕ Ⓖ Ⓗ

5. The <u>lam</u> is with the <u>other</u> <u>farmer</u>.
      A   B   C

NONE
5. Ⓐ Ⓑ Ⓒ Ⓓ

6. It will cost a <u>nickle</u> <u>instead</u> of one <u>cent</u>.
          E   F   G

NONE
6. Ⓔ Ⓕ Ⓖ Ⓗ

7. A <u>lady</u> said to save <u>munny</u> a <u>penny</u> at a time.
    A   B   C

NONE
7. Ⓐ Ⓑ Ⓒ Ⓓ

8. For a <u>kwarter</u> and <u>dime</u>, a <u>farmer</u> gave us milk.
       E   F   G

NONE
8. Ⓔ Ⓕ Ⓖ Ⓗ

9. The <u>lamb</u> was <u>over</u> in the <u>hi</u> grass.
      A   B   C

NONE
9. Ⓐ Ⓑ Ⓒ Ⓓ

Go on ➡

Book 2.1/Unit 3 Review Test

10. The <u>farmr</u> is <u>happy</u> with the <u>weather</u>.
     E   F   G

10. Ⓔ   Ⓕ   Ⓖ   Ⓗ NONE

11. The <u>leter</u> you <u>wrote</u> made her <u>happy</u>.
     A   B   C

11. Ⓐ   Ⓑ   Ⓒ   Ⓓ NONE

12. Let us play <u>over</u> at the <u>other</u> park <u>insted</u>.
           E   F   G

12. Ⓔ   Ⓕ   Ⓖ   Ⓗ NONE

13. <u>Money</u> did not make the <u>lady</u> <u>happy</u>.
   A   B   C

13. Ⓐ   Ⓑ   Ⓒ   Ⓓ NONE

14. The <u>lamb</u> bent its <u>knee</u> <u>ovr</u> the gate.
     E   F G

14. Ⓔ   Ⓕ   Ⓖ   Ⓗ NONE

15. We <u>spread</u> <u>mony</u> over the <u>table</u>.
      A   B   C

15. Ⓐ   Ⓑ   Ⓒ   Ⓓ NONE

16. Do a <u>dime</u> and a <u>nickle</u> make a <u>quarter</u>?
       E   F   G

16. Ⓔ   Ⓕ   Ⓖ   Ⓗ NONE

17. The <u>lady</u> needs one more <u>dyme</u> for <u>bread</u>.
     A   B   C

17. Ⓐ   Ⓑ   Ⓒ   Ⓓ NONE

18. "I like the <u>weather</u> <u>high</u> in the hills," he <u>wrote</u>.
            E   F   G

18. Ⓔ   Ⓕ   Ⓖ   Ⓗ NONE

19. The corn is <u>knee</u> <u>high</u> because of bad <u>weather</u>.
             A B   C

19. Ⓐ   Ⓑ   Ⓒ   Ⓓ NONE

20. The <u>laydy</u> is at the <u>other</u> <u>high</u> school.
     E   F G

20. Ⓔ   Ⓕ   Ⓖ   Ⓗ NONE

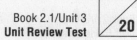

McGraw-Hill School Division

Words with /ů/*oo*

Pretest Directions

Fold back the paper along the dotted line. Use the blanks to write each word as it is read aloud. When you finish the test, unfold the paper. Use the list to the right to correct any spelling mistakes. Practice the words you missed for the Posttest.

To Parents,

Here are the results of your child's weekly spelling Pretest. You can help your child study for the Posttest by following these simple steps for each word on the list:

1. Read the word to your child.

2. Have your child write the word, saying each letter as it is written.

3. Say each letter of the word as your child checks the spelling.

4. If a mistake has been made, have your child read each letter of the correctly spelled word aloud and then repeat steps 1–3.

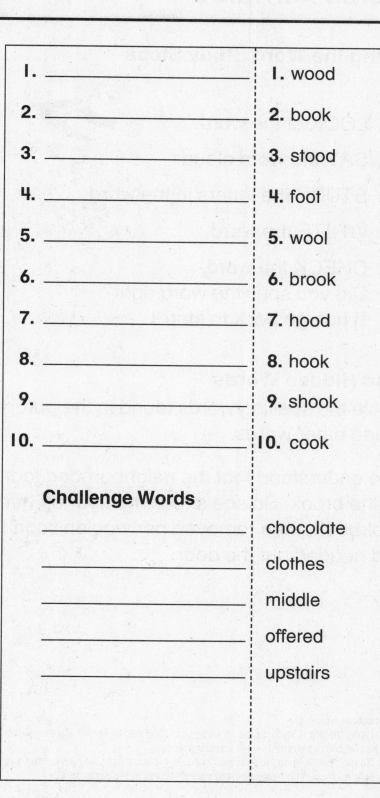

1. _____   1. wood
2. _____   2. book
3. _____   3. stood
4. _____   4. foot
5. _____   5. wool
6. _____   6. brook
7. _____   7. hood
8. _____   8. hook
9. _____   9. shook
10. _____   10. cook

Challenge Words

_____   chocolate

_____   clothes

_____   middle

_____   offered

_____   upstairs

Words with /u̇/oo

Using the Word Study Steps

1. LOOK at the word.

2. SAY the word aloud.

3. STUDY the letters in the word.

4. WRITE the word.

5. CHECK the word.
   Did you spell the word right?
   If not, go back to step 1.

Spelling Tip

Study words that do not match spelling patterns or rules. Use your word study steps.
Examples:
foot, feet
stand, **stood**
shake, **shook**

Find Hidden Words

Circle the spelling words found in the paragraph. Some are hidden inside other words.

She understood that the neighborhood football game was played by the brook. So she shook the flour off her hands, closed the cookbook, then removed her woolen scarf from its wooden hook and headed out the door.

To Parents or Helpers:
   Using the Word Study Steps above as your child comes across any new words will help him or her spell well. Review the steps as you both go over this week's spelling words.
   Go over the Spelling Tip with your child. Help him or her study words that do not match spelling patterns or rules.
   Help your child find and circle the spelling words in the paragraph.

McGraw-Hill School Division

Book 2.2/Unit 1
Charlie Anderson
10

Words with /u̇/oo

wood	stood	wool	hood	shook
book	foot	brook	hook	cook

Look at the spelling words in the box. Match the spelling word with the spelling pattern and write the word.

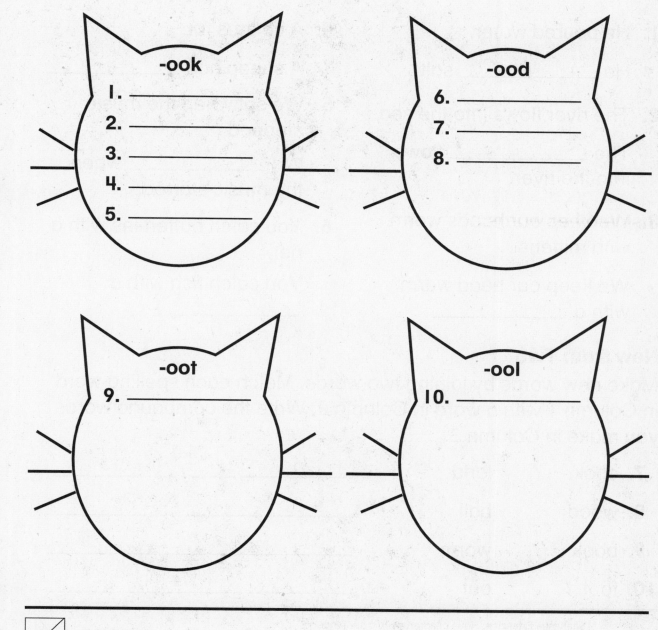

-ook
1. _____
2. _____
3. _____
4. _____
5. _____

-ood
6. _____
7. _____
8. _____

-oot
9. _____

-ool
10. _____

Words with /ŭ/*oo*

wood	stood	wool	hood	shook
book	foot	brook	hook	cook

Make a Connection

Write a spelling word to complete each pair of sentences.

1. He poured water.

   He _____ salt.

2. The river flows into the sea.

   The _____ flows into the river.

3. We keep our hands warm with mittens.

   We keep our head warm with a _____.

4. A cat has fur.

   A sheep has _____.

5. We sat when the music stopped.

   We _____ when the music started.

6. You catch butterflies with a net.

   You catch fish with a _____.

New from Two

Make new words by joining two words. Match each spelling word in Column 1 with a word in Column 2. Write the compound words you make in Column 3.

7. cook   land   _____

8. wood   ball   _____

9. book   worm   _____

10. foot   out   _____

Challenge Extension: Have children write a sentence that uses at least two of the challenge words. Have volunteers read their sentences aloud to the class.

McGraw-Hill School Division

Words with /ŭ/oo

Proofreading Activity

There are six spelling mistakes in the letter below. Circle each misspelled word. Write the words correctly on the lines below.

Dear Sue,

I am having fun at camp. Today, I stude by a bruk and saw two little frogs jumping. Tonight we are going to cooke outside. We found wud to make a fire. I am glad my jacket has a hoode because it gets cold here at night. I haven't had time yet to read the buk you gave me, but I plan to start it soon. I miss you.

> Your friend,
> May

1. _____ 2. _____ 3. _____

4. _____ 5. _____ 6. _____

Writing Activity

Write a letter to May using four spelling words. Tell about something that happened at home.
Circle the spelling words that you use in your letter.

_____

_____

_____

_____

_____

Words with /ù/oo

Look at the words in each set. One word in each set is spelled correctly. Use a pencil to color in the circle in front of that word. Before you begin, look at the sample sets of words. Sample A has been done for you. Do Sample B by yourself. When you are sure you know what to do, you may go on with the rest of the page.

Sample A
- (A) luk
- (B) looke
- (C) look
- (D) loke

Sample B
- (E) party
- (F) paety
- (G) partee
- (H) parte

1.
- (A) wood
- (B) woodd
- (C) wud
- (D) wuud

2.
- (E) stude
- (F) stood
- (G) stodd
- (H) stuud

3.
- (A) fut
- (B) fout
- (C) foot
- (D) foote

4.
- (E) hoode
- (F) hood
- (G) huod
- (H) huud

5.
- (A) brook
- (B) broock
- (C) bruuk
- (D) brouke

6.
- (E) shuk
- (F) shook
- (G) shoock
- (H) shooke

7.
- (A) wuul
- (B) wool
- (C) wooll
- (D) wul

8.
- (E) booke
- (F) book
- (G) buk
- (H) buuk

9.
- (A) cooke
- (B) cuuk
- (C) cuk
- (D) cook

10.
- (E) huk
- (F) hooke
- (G) hooc
- (H) hook

Words with Soft *c* and Soft *g*

Pretest Directions

Fold back the paper along the dotted line. Use the blanks to write each word as it is read aloud. When you finish the test, unfold the paper. Use the list to the right to correct any spelling mistakes. Practice the words you missed for the Posttest.

To Parents,

Here are the results of your child's weekly spelling Pretest. You can help your child study for the Posttest by following these simple steps for each word on the list:

1. Read the word to your child.

2. Have your child write the word, saying each letter as it is written.

3. Say each letter of the word as your child checks the spelling.

4. If a mistake has been made, have your child read each letter of the correctly spelled word aloud and then repeat steps 1–3.

1. _____ 1. dance

2. _____ 2. age

3. _____ 3. rice

4. _____ 4. mice

5. _____ 5. charge

6. _____ 6. race

7. _____ 7. space

8. _____ 8. cage

9. _____ 9. large

10. _____ 10. page

Challenge Words

_____ diving

_____ explains

_____ harm

_____ soil

_____ village

10 Book 2.2/Unit 1
Fernando's Gift

Words with Soft *c* and Soft *g*

Using the Word Study Steps

1. LOOK at the word.

2. SAY the word aloud.

3. STUDY the letters in the word.

4. WRITE the word.

5. CHECK the word.
   Did you spell the word right?
   If not, go back to step 1.

Spelling Tip

When the /s/ sound is spelled c, c is always followed by **e**, **i**, or **y**.
Examples:
   ri**ce**   dan**ce**

When /j/ is spelled **g**, **g** is always followed by **e**, **i**, or **y**.
Examples:
   ca**ge**   char**ge**

Find and Circle

Where are the spelling words?

a	b	r	i	c	e	c	c	h	a	r	g	e	d
g	d	a	n	c	e	a	r	o	m	k	j	g	f
e	s	c	r	p	a	g	e	y	s	p	a	c	e
w	y	e	m	i	c	e	u	l	a	r	g	e	t

To Parents or Helpers:
   Using the Word Study Steps above as your child comes across any new words will help him or her spell well. Review the steps as you both go over this week's spelling words.
   Go over the Spelling Tip with your child. Ask if he or she knows other words that rhyme with the spelling words.
   Help your child find and circle the spelling words in the puzzle.

Words with Soft *c* and Soft *g*

dance	rice	charge	space	large
age	mice	race	cage	page

How Nice!

Say each spelling word. Listen to how it ends. Match each word with the spelling pattern. Then, write the word under the correct pattern.

ce   ge

1. _____   6. _____

2. _____   7. _____

3. _____   8. _____

4. _____   9. _____

5. _____   10. _____

The letter **e** after the letter **g** gives it the soft **g** sound. Look at each pair of words.

Circle the word that has the sound of soft **g**.

11. pig   page   **12.** rage   rag

The letter **e** after the letter **c** gives it the soft **c** sound. Look at each pair of words.

Circle the word that has the sound of soft **c**.

13. race   rack   **14.** sick   space

Words with Soft *c* and Soft *g*

dance	rice	charge	space	large
age	mice	race	cage	page

Write a spelling word to complete each sentence.

1. I'd like to see a rocket fly off into _____.

2. What _____ will you be next year?

3. What do you feed those little white _____?

4. He has very _____ brown eyes.

5. Mom made red beans and _____ for dinner.

6. At the zoo, animals are in a _____.

7. The last _____ of the book is missing.

Make a new word by dropping **e** and adding **ing** to the spelling words below.

8. charge − e + ing = _____

9. race − e + ing = _____

10. dance − e + ing = _____

Challenge Extension: Have children write a brief story about helping save a natural resource. Ask them to use at least three of the Challenge Words.

106

Book 2.2/Unit 1
Fernando's Gift

10

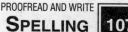

Words with Soft *c* and Soft *g*

Proofreading Activity

There are six spelling mistakes in the paragraph below. Circle each misspelled word. Write the words correctly on the lines below.

Our class has three brown mise. Two are small, so we think they are babies. We are not sure of their agee. Susan brought a caje for them to live in. The biggest mouse seems to be in charje. The others follow what he does. The mice like to danse when we have music. They also like to run. When we put them on the floor, they rase around as fast as they can go.

1. _____ 2. _____ 3. _____

4. _____ 5. _____ 6. _____

Writing Activity

Pets in the classroom are fun. What are some animals that could be a class pet? Write about having a class pet. Use four spelling words. Circle the spelling words you use.

_____

_____

_____

_____

Words with Soft *c* and Soft *g*

Look at the words in each set. One word in each set is spelled correctly. Use a pencil to color in the circle in front of that word. Before you begin, look at the sample sets of words. Sample A has been done for you. Do Sample B by yourself. When you are sure you know what to do, you may go on with the rest of the page.

Sample A
- (A) nice
- (B) nic
- (C) nise
- (D) niss

Sample B
- (E) mann
- (F) mahn
- (G) man
- (H) mahne

1. (A) caj
    (B) cage
    (C) caaget
    (D) caje

2. (E) rice
    (F) risse
    (G) ris
    (H) ricce

3. (A) charj
    (B) charg
    (C) charje
    (D) charge

4. (E) danse
    (F) dans
    (G) dance
    (H) danc

5. (A) page
    (B) paje
    (C) paag
    (D) paaj

6. (E) mice
    (F) mies
    (G) mics
    (H) miis

7. (A) larj
    (B) larg
    (C) larje
    (D) large

8. (E) aij
    (F) aig
    (G) age
    (H) aje

9. (A) race
    (B) raice
    (C) rase
    (D) rass

10. (E) spase
    (F) space
    (G) spass
    (H) spac

McGraw-Hill School Division

Words with /ô/ *a, aw, au, augh*

Pretest Directions

Fold back the paper along the dotted line. Use the blanks to write each word as it is read aloud. When you finish the test, unfold the paper. Use the list to the right to correct any spelling mistakes. Practice the words you missed for the Posttest.

To Parents,

Here are the results of your child's weekly spelling Pretest. You can help your child study for the Posttest by following these simple steps for each word on the list:

1. Read the word to your child.

2. Have your child write the word, saying each letter as it is written.

3. Say each letter of the word as your child checks the spelling.

4. If a mistake has been made, have your child read each letter of the correctly spelled word aloud and then repeat steps 1–3.

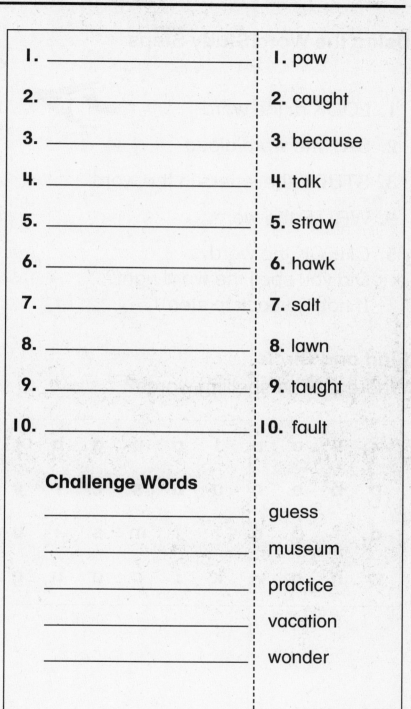

1. _____ 1. paw

2. _____ 2. caught

3. _____ 3. because

4. _____ 4. talk

5. _____ 5. straw

6. _____ 6. hawk

7. _____ 7. salt

8. _____ 8. lawn

9. _____ 9. taught

10. _____ 10. fault

Challenge Words

_____ guess

_____ museum

_____ practice

_____ vacation

_____ wonder

Words with /ô/ *a, aw, au, augh*

Using the Word Study Steps

1. LOOK at the word.
2. SAY the word aloud.
3. STUDY the letters in the word.
4. WRITE the word.
5. CHECK the word.
   Did you spell the word right?
   If not, go back to step 1.

Spelling Tip

Keep a Personal Word List in a notebook. Write words you have trouble spelling.

Find and Circle
Where are the spelling words?

x	v	o	u	t	a	u	g	h	t	i	b	p	n	l
p	b	e	c	a	u	s	e	r	s	a	l	t	t	a
a	f	a	u	l	t	m	s	l	u	s	t	r	a	w
w	h	a	w	k	r	c	a	u	g	h	t	v	c	n

To Parents or Helpers:
Using the Word Study Steps above as your child comes across any new words will help him or her spell well. Review the steps as you both go over this week's spelling words.
Go over the Spelling Tip with your child. Help your child write words that they have trouble spelling in a notebook that they can keep.
Help your child find and circle the spelling words in the puzzle.

McGraw-Hill School Division

Words with /ô/ *a, aw, au, augh*

paw	because	straw	salt	taught
caught	talk	hawk	lawn	fault

Look at the spelling words in the box.

Find a spelling pattern for each word. Match the word with a spelling pattern. Then write the word on the lines below.

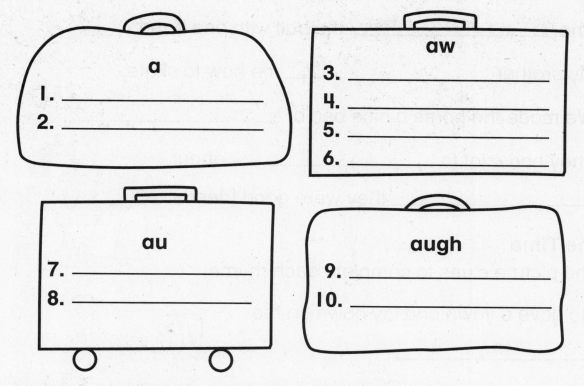

a

1. _____
2. _____

aw

3. _____
4. _____
5. _____
6. _____

au

7. _____
8. _____

augh

9. _____
10. _____

Circle the spelling patterns of /ô/ in each suitcase.

11. Where did you find /ô/ spelled **aw** in the spelling words? Circle the answer.

at the beginning   in the middle   at the end

12. Where did you find /ô/ spelled **a**, **au**, or **augh** in the spelling words? Circle the answer.

at the beginning   in the middle   at the end

Words with /ô/ *a, aw, au, augh*

paw	because	straw	salt	taught
caught	talk	hawk	lawn	fault

Write a spelling word to complete each sentence.

1. The dog gave me its _____ to shake.

2. She _____ the ball with one hand.

3. My brother _____ me how to skate.

4. We made the horse a nice bed of _____.

5. They had a lot to _____ about

   _____ they were good friends.

Rhyme Time

Use the picture clues to complete each rhyme.

6. He gave a yawn and lay down on the

   _____.

7. It wasn't my _____ that I spilled

   the _____.

8. The _____ flew high in the big blue sky.

Challenge Extension: Have children write a journal entry about an imaginary vacation they would like to take. Ask them to use at least three Challenge Words.

McGraw-Hill School Division

Words with /ô/ *a, aw, au, augh*

Proofreading Activity

There are six spelling mistakes in the paragraph below.
Circle each misspelled word. Write the words correctly on
the lines below.

People always tawk about how smart dogs are. Jamal taut his dog
how to shake hands with his pau. Jamal's dog liked to play in the
barn. One day the dog got cawt inside and couldn't get out. It was
Jamal's fawlt becaws he had shut the barn door by mistake.

I. _____ 2. _____ 3. _____

4. _____ 5. _____ 6. _____

Writing Activity

Would you like to visit a farm? Write sentences about a place
that you would like to visit. Use four spelling words from the
spelling list.

_____

_____

_____

_____

_____

Words with /ô/ *a, aw, au, augh*

Look at the words in each set. One word in each set is spelled correctly. Use a pencil to color in the circle in front of that word. Before you begin, look at the sample sets of words. Sample A has been done for you. Do Sample B by yourself. When you are sure you know what to do, you may go on with the rest of the page.

Sample A
- (A) wawk
- (B) waugk
- (C) walk
- (D) wauk

Sample B
- (E) spase
- (F) space
- (G) spas
- (H) spaes

1.
- (A) hauk
- (B) hawk
- (C) haugk
- (D) hak

2.
- (E) taught
- (F) tawt
- (G) taugt
- (H) tawght

3.
- (A) lauun
- (B) laun
- (C) laughn
- (D) lawn

4.
- (E) sault
- (F) saltt
- (G) salt
- (H) sawlt

5.
- (A) paw
- (B) paugh
- (C) pau
- (D) paau

6.
- (E) talk
- (F) taulk
- (G) tawlk
- (H) taughlk

7.
- (A) becauz
- (B) because
- (C) becawse
- (D) becauze

8.
- (E) falt
- (F) fawlt
- (G) faughlt
- (H) fault

9.
- (A) caut
- (B) cawt
- (C) caught
- (D) cawht

10.
- (E) stauw
- (F) straw
- (G) straugh
- (H) staugh

Words with Digraphs *ph*, *tch*, *ch*

Pretest Directions

Fold back the paper along the dotted line. Use the blanks to write each word as it is read aloud. When you finish the test, unfold the paper. Use the list to the right to correct any spelling mistakes. Practice the words you missed for the Posttest.

To Parents,

Here are the results of your child's weekly spelling Pretest. You can help your child study for the Posttest by following these simple steps for each word on the list:

1. Read the word to your child.

2. Have your child write the word, saying each letter as it is written.

3. Say each letter of the word as your child checks the spelling.

4. If a mistake has been made, have your child read each letter of the correctly spelled word aloud and then repeat steps 1–3.

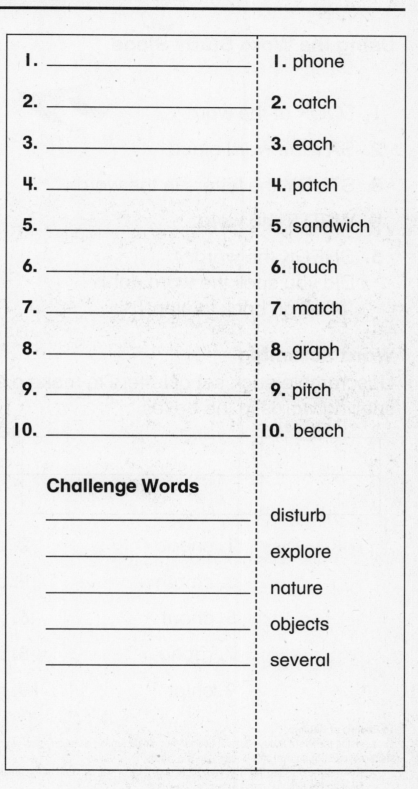

1. _____ 1. phone
2. _____ 2. catch
3. _____ 3. each
4. _____ 4. patch
5. _____ 5. sandwich
6. _____ 6. touch
7. _____ 7. match
8. _____ 8. graph
9. _____ 9. pitch
10. _____ 10. beach

Challenge Words

_____ disturb
_____ explore
_____ nature
_____ objects
_____ several

Words with Digraphs *ph*, *tch*, *ch*

Using the Word Study Steps

1. LOOK at the word.

2. SAY the word aloud.

3. STUDY the letters in the word.

4. WRITE the word.

5. CHECK the word.
   Did you spell the word right?
   If not, go back to step 1.

Spelling Tip

Look for a smaller word in a new word to help you write the new word.

sand + wich = sandwich

Word Scramble

Unscramble each set of letters to make a spelling word. Write the spelling words in the boxes.

1.	2.	3.	4.	5.
6.	7.	8.	9.	10.

1. cheab   **2.** pohne

3. cmath   **4.** chatc

5. chout   **6.** heac

7. rgpha   **8.** pacht

9. chipt   **10.** hicwsand

To Parents or Helpers:

Using the Word Study Steps above as your child comes across any new words will help him or her spell well. Review the steps as you both go over this week's spelling words.

Go over the Spelling Tip with your child. Ask if he or she can find other smaller words in new words.

Help your child unscramble the spelling words.

McGraw-Hill School Division

Words with Digraphs *ph*, *tch*, *ch*

phone	each	sandwich	match	pitch
catch	patch	touch	graph	beach

Pattern Power!

Write the spelling words for each of these patterns.

ph

1. _____

2. _____

tch

3. _____

4. _____

5. _____

6. _____

ch

7. _____

8. _____

9. _____

10. _____

Find Me a Pattern!

Write each word. Circle the letters that are the same.

11. _____   _____

12. _____   _____

13. _____   _____

Rhyme Time

Write the spelling word that rhymes with each of these words.

14. bone _____   15. ditch _____

Words with Digraphs *ph*, *tch*, *ch*

phone	each	sandwich	match	pitch
catch	patch	touch	graph	beach

Write a spelling word to answer each question.

1. How can you talk to a friend? _____

2. What do you sometimes eat for lunch? _____

3. Where can you swim? _____

4. What can you use to fix a rip in your pants? _____

5. What can you use to show data? _____

6. What do people use to start a fire? _____

Use the spelling words to complete the sentences.

7. If you _____ the ball to Sam, he will _____ it.

8. _____ child will be able to _____ the bunny.

New Words

Add **es** to each of these words. Write the new word.

9. match + es = _____

10. patch + es = _____

11. sandwich + es = _____

12. beach + es = _____

McGraw-Hill School Division

Words with Digraphs *ph*, *tch*, *ch*

Proofreading Activity

There are six spelling mistakes in the paragraph below. Circle each misspelled word. Write the words correctly on the lines below.

Every summer my family and I go to the baech. We take lunch with us. Eech of us usually has a peanut butter sandwitch, a glass of lemonade, and some grapes. Then I go to tutch the water. If it is not cold, I go swimming. Last summer I couldn't use my inner tube because it needed a pach. After swimming, we play ball. My father throws and I katch. A day at the beach is a fun time for my family.

1. _____ 2. _____ 3. _____

4. _____ 5. _____ 6. _____

Writing Activity

Write sentences that tell about something that you would like to do next summer. Use four words from the spelling list.

_____

_____

_____

_____

_____

McGraw-Hill School Division

Words with Digraphs *ph*, *tch*, *ch*

Look at the words in each set. One word in each set is spelled correctly. Use a pencil to color in the circle in front of that word. Before you begin, look at the sample sets of words. Sample A has been done for you. Do Sample B by yourself. When you are sure you know what to do, you may go on with the rest of the page.

Sample A
Ⓐ sutch
Ⓑ soch
Ⓒ such
Ⓓ sech

Sample B
Ⓔ tawk
Ⓕ tauk
Ⓖ talk
Ⓗ tolk

1. Ⓐ pich
    Ⓑ phitch
    Ⓒ pitch
    Ⓓ petch

2. Ⓔ graf
    Ⓕ graph
    Ⓖ grafph
    Ⓗ grph

3. Ⓐ tuch
    Ⓑ toutch
    Ⓒ touch
    Ⓓ tutch

4. Ⓔ patch
    Ⓕ pach
    Ⓖ phatch
    Ⓗ petch

5. Ⓐ beesh
    Ⓑ betch
    Ⓒ beatch
    Ⓓ beach

6. Ⓔ fone
    Ⓕ phone
    Ⓖ fhone
    Ⓗ phon

7. Ⓐ sanwich
    Ⓑ sandwitch
    Ⓒ sanwhich
    Ⓓ sandwich

8. Ⓔ cach
    Ⓕ catch
    Ⓖ chatch
    Ⓗ cetch

9. Ⓐ eech
    Ⓑ each
    Ⓒ eatch
    Ⓓ eetch

10. Ⓔ mach
    Ⓕ maach
    Ⓖ metch
    Ⓗ match

Words From Science

Pretest Directions

Fold back the paper along the dotted line. Use the blanks to write each word as it is read aloud. When you finish the test, unfold the paper. Use the list to the right to correct any spelling mistakes. Practice the words you missed for the Posttest.

To Parents,

Here are the results of your child's weekly spelling Pretest. You can help your child study for the Posttest by following these simple steps for each word on the list:

1. Read the word to your child.

2. Have your child write the word, saying each letter as it is written.

3. Say each letter of the word as your child checks the spelling.

4. If a mistake has been made, have your child read each letter of the correctly spelled word aloud and then repeat steps 1–3.

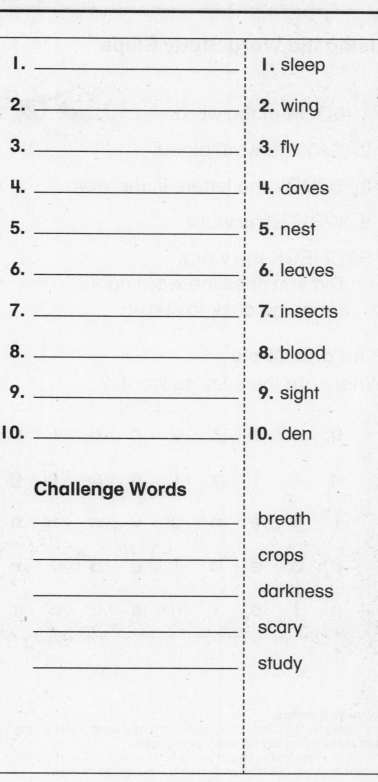

1. _____   1. sleep

2. _____   2. wing

3. _____   3. fly

4. _____   4. caves

5. _____   5. nest

6. _____   6. leaves

7. _____   7. insects

8. _____   8. blood

9. _____   9. sight

10. _____   10. den

Challenge Words

_____ breath

_____ crops

_____ darkness

_____ scary

_____ study

Words From Science

Using the Word Study Steps

1. LOOK at the word.

2. SAY the word aloud.

3. STUDY the letters in the word.

4. WRITE the word.

5. CHECK the word.
   Did you spell the word right?
   If not, go back to step 1.

Spelling Tip

When a base word ends with a consonant followed by **y**, change the **y** to **i** when adding the ending.

fly + es = fl**i**es

Find and Circle

Where are the spelling words?

```
n  e  s  t  v  c  b  l  o  o  d  l  l  o
q  f  l  y  i  a  s  i  g  h  t  h  g  v
r  d  e  n  b  v  w  i  n  g  a  a  n  h
d  a  e  h  l  e  a  v  e  s  k  i  l  m
p  l  p  i  n  s  e  c  t  s  r  r  c  o
```

To Parents or Helpers:
   Using the Word Study Steps above as your child comes across any new words will help him or her spell well. Review the steps as you both go over this week's spelling words.
   Go over the Spelling Tip with your child. Ask your child if he or she knows other base words that end with a consonant followed by **y**. Help your child change the **y** to **i** when adding the ending.
   Help your child find and circle the spelling words in the puzzle.

McGraw-Hill School Division

Words From Science

sleep	fly	nest	insects	sight
wing	caves	leaves	blood	den

The words *cat* and *when* have short vowel sounds. The words *cake* and *seen* have long vowel sounds.

Write the spelling words with short vowel sounds and then write the spelling words with long vowel sounds in the bats below.

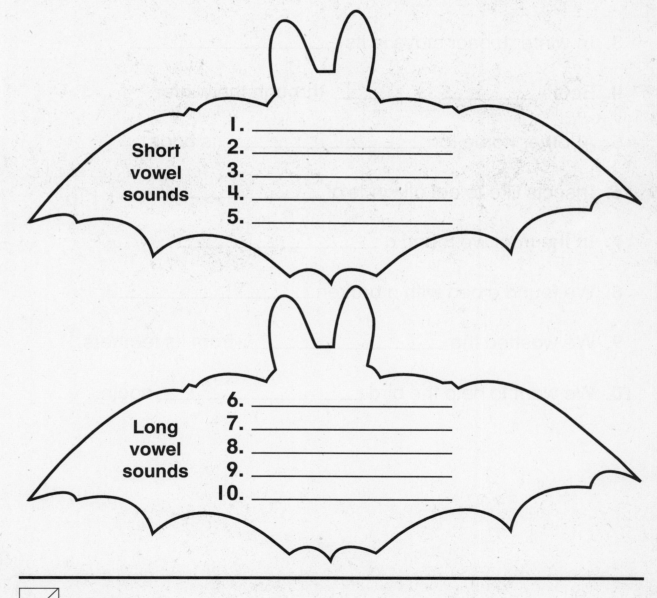

Short vowel sounds

1. _____
2. _____
3. _____
4. _____
5. _____

Long vowel sounds

6. _____
7. _____
8. _____
9. _____
10. _____

Words From Science

sleep	fly	nest	insects	sight
wing	caves	leaves	blood	den

Write a spelling word to complete each sentence.

1. Bats sometimes live in _____.

2. Bats are not known for their sense of _____.

3. In winter a bear stays in its _____.

4. Bears _____ through the winter.

5. Another name for _____ is bugs.

6. Insects like to eat all kinds of _____.

7. In the tree, we found a _____.

8. We found a bird with a broken _____.

9. We washed the _____ from its feathers.

10. We want to help the bird _____ again.

Words From Science

Proofreading Activity

There are six spelling mistakes in the story. Circle each misspelled word. Write the words correctly on the lines below.

A bird uses leafs and twigs to build its nesst. Birds are good parents. They bring worms and insecs to their babies. It can be a funny site to watch a baby bird learn to flie. At first, baby birds are not very good at flying. They flap their wengs and nothing happens. They try again and again until they finally take off into the air.

1. _____ 2. _____ 3. _____

4. _____ 5. _____ 6. _____

Writing Activity

Write a story about nature. Use four spelling words in your story. Circle the spelling words in your story.

_____

_____

_____

_____

_____

Words From Science

Look at the words in each set. One word in each set is spelled correctly. Use a pencil to color in the circle in front of that word. Before you begin, look at the sample sets of words. Sample A has been done for you. Do Sample B by yourself. When you are sure you know what to do, you may go on with the rest of the page.

Sample A
- (A) sunn
- (B) sone
- (C) sun
- (D) sune

Sample B
- (E) beeche
- (F) baech
- (G) beache
- (H) beach

1. (A) leafes
   (B) leaves
   (C) leeves
   (D) leavs

2. (E) weng
   (F) winng
   (G) winge
   (H) wing

3. (A) sihgt
   (B) siight
   (C) sight
   (D) siet

4. (E) nesst
   (F) nest
   (G) neste
   (H) neess

5. (A) caves
   (B) caavs
   (C) cavs
   (D) cavas

6. (E) slepe
   (F) slep
   (G) sleep
   (H) sleepe

7. (A) insectx
   (B) insects
   (C) inseects
   (D) insecks

8. (E) blud
   (F) blod
   (G) bluud
   (H) blood

9. (A) fly
   (B) fliy
   (C) fli
   (D) flie

10. (E) dehn
    (F) den
    (G) denn
    (H) denne

McGraw-Hill School Division

Book 2.2/Unit I Review Test

Read each sentence. If an underlined word is spelled wrong, fill in the circle that goes with that word. If no word is spelled wrong, fill in the circle below NONE.
Read Sample A, and do Sample B.

A. I <u>took</u> <u>cheese</u> to the <u>nice</u> lady.
    A   B   C

A. Ⓐ Ⓑ Ⓒ ● (NONE)

B. <u>Look</u> at him <u>catch</u> the ball and <u>walk</u> away.
    E   F   G

B. Ⓔ Ⓕ Ⓖ Ⓗ (NONE)

1. <u>Because</u> she hurt her <u>foot</u>, she didn't <u>danse</u>.
    A   B   C

1. Ⓐ Ⓑ Ⓒ Ⓓ (NONE)

2. He wants to <u>talk</u> about the <u>leafes</u> in the <u>caves</u>.
          E   F   G

2. Ⓔ Ⓕ Ⓖ Ⓗ (NONE)

3. I will <u>cook</u> <u>rice</u> and make a <u>sandwich</u>.
          A   B   C

3. Ⓐ Ⓑ Ⓒ Ⓓ (NONE)

4. The bird <u>cauwt</u> its <u>wing</u> in the <u>wood</u> door.
            E   F   G

4. Ⓔ Ⓕ Ⓖ Ⓗ (NONE)

5. Please don't <u>tuch</u> the <u>leaves</u> in the <u>nest</u>.
                A   B   C

5. Ⓐ Ⓑ Ⓒ Ⓓ (NONE)

6. I won't <u>charge</u> for the <u>wool</u> hat with the <u>pach</u>.
            E   F   G

6. Ⓔ Ⓕ Ⓖ Ⓗ (NONE)

7. The dog tried to <u>tuch</u> the <u>cage</u> with its <u>paw</u>.
                    A   B   C

7. Ⓐ Ⓑ Ⓒ Ⓓ (NONE)

8. The <u>graph</u> shows the <u>nist</u> with the most <u>leaves</u>.
          E   F   G

8. Ⓔ Ⓕ Ⓖ Ⓗ (NONE)

9. I will <u>cook</u> <u>rise</u> and put it near the <u>cage</u>.
            A   B   C

9. Ⓐ Ⓑ Ⓒ Ⓓ (NONE)

Go on

Book 2.2/Unit I Review Test

10. <u>Becawse</u> it's cold I wore my <u>wool</u> hat to the <u>caves</u>.
     E   F   G
10. Ⓔ   Ⓕ   Ⓖ   NONE Ⓗ

11. Don't <u>touch</u> the <u>sandwitch</u> with your <u>foot</u>!
          A   B   C
11. Ⓐ   Ⓑ   Ⓒ   NONE Ⓓ

12. The <u>wood</u> <u>dance</u> floor needed a <u>patch</u>.
      E   F   G
12. Ⓔ   Ⓕ   Ⓖ   NONE Ⓗ

13. I <u>charje</u> a dime for the <u>nest</u> made of <u>leaves</u>.
    A   B   C
13. Ⓐ   Ⓑ   Ⓒ   NONE Ⓓ

14. I drew a <u>paw</u> and a <u>weng</u> on the <u>graph</u>.
          E   F   G
14. Ⓔ   Ⓕ   Ⓖ   NONE Ⓗ

15. The <u>cook</u> <u>caught</u> his <u>fooot</u> in the door.
     A   B   C
15. Ⓐ   Ⓑ   Ⓒ   NONE Ⓓ

16. Let's <u>tawk</u> about the <u>charge</u> for the <u>rice</u>.
     E   F   G
16. Ⓔ   Ⓕ   Ⓖ   NONE Ⓗ

17. I pushed the <u>woud</u> in the <u>cage</u> with my <u>foot</u>.
         A   B   C
17. Ⓐ   Ⓑ   Ⓒ   NONE Ⓓ

18. I will <u>talk</u> about the <u>woole</u> dress at the <u>dance</u>.
     E   F   G
18. Ⓔ   Ⓕ   Ⓖ   NONE Ⓗ

19. The <u>sandwich</u> is good <u>because</u> of the <u>cooke</u>.
    A   B   C
19. Ⓐ   Ⓑ   Ⓒ   NONE Ⓓ

20. The dog in the <u>cage</u> had a <u>patch</u> on his <u>pauw</u>.
        E   F   G
20. Ⓔ   Ⓕ   Ⓖ   NONE Ⓗ

McGraw-Hill School Division

Words with *c*, *k*, and *ck*

Pretest Directions

Fold back your paper along the dotted line. Use the blanks to write each word as it is said to you. When you finish the test, unfold the paper and correct any spelling mistakes. Practice those words for the Posttest.

To Parents,

Here are the results of your child's weekly spelling Pretest. You can help your child study for the Posttest by following these simple steps for each word on the word list:

1. Read the word to your child.

2. Have your child write the word, saying each letter as it is written.

3. Say each letter of the word as your child checks the spelling.

4. If a mistake has been made, have your child read each letter of the correctly spelled word aloud and then repeat steps 1–3.

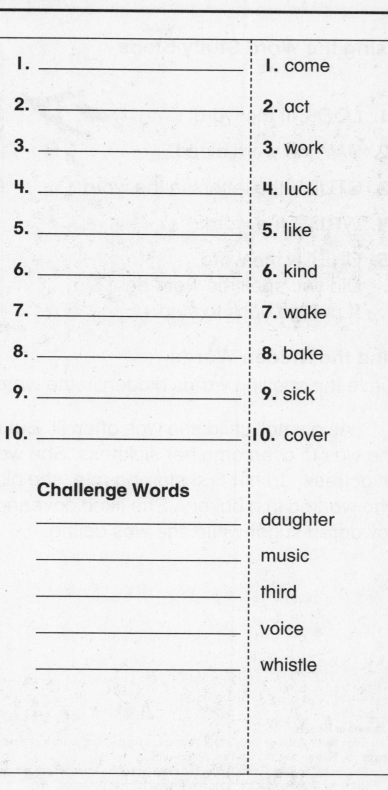

1. _____ | 1. come
2. _____ | 2. act
3. _____ | 3. work
4. _____ | 4. luck
5. _____ | 5. like
6. _____ | 6. kind
7. _____ | 7. wake
8. _____ | 8. bake
9. _____ | 9. sick
10. _____ | 10. cover

Challenge Words

_____ daughter

_____ music

_____ third

_____ voice

_____ whistle

McGraw-Hill School Division

Words with *c*, *k*, and *ck*

Using the Word Study Steps

1. LOOK at the word.

2. SAY the word aloud.

3. STUDY the letters in the word.

4. WRITE the word.

5. CHECK the word.
   Did you spell the word right?
   If not, go back to step 1.

Spelling Tip

The **ck** spelling of the sound /k/ appears only at the end of a word or syllable and never appears at the beginning of a word. Examples:
lu**ck**, du**ck**

Find the Hidden Words

Circle the spelling words hidden in the words of the paragraph.

As a small child she was often ill. But when she grew older, she was to overcome her sickness. She was lucky. She became an actress. In her first starring role, she played a kind old woman who worked in a bakery. She liked covering the doughnuts in powdered sugar while she was acting.

To Parents or Helpers:
Using the Word Study Steps above as your child comes across any new words will help him or her spell well. Review the steps as you both go over this week's spelling words.
Go over the Spelling Tip with your child. Have him or her list other words ending with **ck**.
Help your child find and circle the spelling words in the paragraph.

Words with *c*, *k*, and *ck*

come	work	like	wake	sick
act	luck	kind	bake	cover

Pattern Smart

Write the words with **c**.

1. _____

2. _____

3. _____

Write the words with **ck**.

4. _____

5. _____

Write the words with **k**.

6. _____

7. _____

8. _____

9. _____

10. _____

Which spelling of the sound /k/ only appears at the end of a word or syllable and never appears at the beginning of a word?

11. _____

Write two spelling words that end with that spelling.

12. _____   13. _____

14. Write the spelling word that completes this rhyme.

Tick Tock   Tock Tick

Says the clock.   The clock is _____.

Words with *c*, *k*, and *ck*

come	work	like	wake	sick
act	luck	kind	bake	cover

Write the words that complete each sentence.

1. My father rides the bus to _____.

2. What _____ of sandwich do you want?

3. You should _____ your mouth when
you sneeze.

4. Tony likes to _____ cookies.

5. It's time to _____ up from your nap.

6. Is Maria _____ with a cold?

Word Meaning

Say it another way. Draw a line from each spelling word to the
word that means almost the same.

7. kind   cook

8. cover   ill

9. bake   lid

10. sick   nice

Challenge Extension: Have students write fill-in
sentences using the words. They may exchange
with a partner to complete the sentences.

McGraw-Hill School Division

Name _____ Date _____

Words with *c*, *k*, and *ck*

Proofreading Activity

There are six spelling mistakes in the paragraph below. Circle each misspelled word. Write the words correctly on the lines below.

It takes a lot of werk to make cookies. Pat asked her friend May to cume help. "What keind shall we make?" May asked. "I like chocolate chip!" Pat said. Pat's father put the cookies in the oven to backe. "Waak me when they are done," he said. Pat told May to cuver some cookies and take them home to her mother.

1. _____   2. _____   3. _____

4. _____   5. _____   6. _____

Writing Activity

Write a recipe using four spelling words. Circle the spelling words in your recipe.

_____

_____

_____

_____

_____

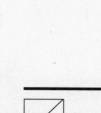

Words with *c*, *k*, and *ck*

Look at the words in each set. One word in each set is spelled correctly. Use a pencil to color in the circle in front of that word. Before you begin, look at the sample sets of words. Sample A has been done for you. Do Sample B by yourself. When you are sure you know what to do, you may go on with the rest of the page.

Sample A
- (A) taak
- (B) tayk
- (C) take
- (D) teake

Sample B
- (E) cage
- (F) caage
- (G) caje
- (H) cayge

1.
- (A) akt
- (B) ackt
- (C) act
- (D) acck

2.
- (E) waik
- (F) wacke
- (G) wayke
- (H) wake

3.
- (A) kind
- (B) kined
- (C) kaned
- (D) keind

4.
- (E) come
- (F) kome
- (G) cume
- (H) kum

5.
- (A) lauk
- (B) luk
- (C) luck
- (D) louck

6.
- (E) cowver
- (F) cover
- (G) cuver
- (H) coover

7.
- (A) woirk
- (B) work
- (C) worck
- (D) worek

8.
- (E) bake
- (F) beik
- (G) bayk
- (H) baik

9.
- (A) seak
- (B) sikc
- (C) seeck
- (D) sick

10.
- (E) leik
- (F) like
- (G) licke
- (H) lyke

McGraw-Hill School Division

Words with Blends *bl*, *br*, *dr*, *pl*, and *tr*

Pretest Directions

Fold back your paper along the dotted line. Use the blanks to write each word as it is said to you. When you finish the test, unfold the paper and correct any spelling mistakes. Practice those words for the Posttest.

To Parents,

Here are the results of your child's weekly spelling Pretest. You can help your child study for the Posttest by following these simple steps for each word on the word list:

1. Read the word to your child.

2. Have your child write the word, saying each letter as it is written.

3. Say each letter of the word as your child checks the spelling.

4. If a mistake has been made, have your child read each letter of the correctly spelled word aloud and then repeat steps 1–3.

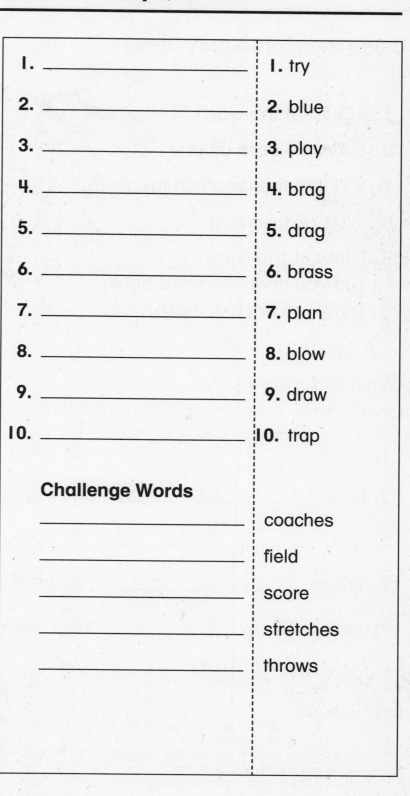

1. _____   1. try

2. _____   2. blue

3. _____   3. play

4. _____   4. brag

5. _____   5. drag

6. _____   6. brass

7. _____   7. plan

8. _____   8. blow

9. _____   9. draw

10. _____   10. trap

Challenge Words

_____   coaches

_____   field

_____   score

_____   stretches

_____   throws

Words with Blends

Using the Word Study Steps

1. LOOK at the word.

2. SAY the word aloud.

3. STUDY the letters in the word.

4. WRITE the word.

5. CHECK the word.
   Did you spell the word right?
   If not, go back to step 1.

Spelling Tip

When a one- syllable word ends in one vowel followed by one consonant, double the consonant before adding an ending that begins with a vowel.

brag + ing = bragging
drag + ed = dragged

Word Scramble

Unscramble each set of letters to make a spelling word.

1. uelb _____

2. wrad _____

3. layp _____

4. prat _____

5. grab _____

6. rty _____

7. srabs _____

8. grad _____

9. wolb _____

10. nlap _____

To Parents or Helpers:

Using the Word Study Steps above as your child comes across any new words will help him or her spell well. Review the steps as you both go over this week's spelling words.

Go over the Spelling Tip with your child. Ask your child to find other new one syllable words that double the final consonant before adding an ending that begins with a vowel.

Help your child unscramble the letters to spell words.

McGraw-Hill School Division

Words with Blends *bl*, *br*, *dr*, *pl*, and *tr*

try	play	drag	plan	draw
blue	brag	brass	blow	trap

Plain Plates

Find the spelling words that begin with each of the sounds below.
Write each word in the correct plate.

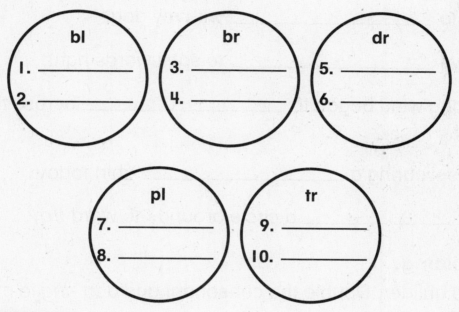

bl
1. _____
2. _____

br
3. _____
4. _____

dr
5. _____
6. _____

pl
7. _____
8. _____

tr
9. _____
10. _____

Pattern Smart

Write the spelling words that have the same pattern as **drip**.

11. _____   12. _____

Write the spelling words that have the same pattern as **trip**.

13. _____   14. _____

Circle the letters that spell the patterns.

15. Where do these letters appear? Circle the answer.

    at the beginning   in the middle   at the end

Words with Blends *bl*, *br*, *dr*, *pl*, and *tr*

try	play	drag	plan	draw
blue	brag	brass	blow	trap

Use a spelling word to complete each sentence.

1. The school bell was made of _____.

2. I like to _____ with my dog.

3. Always _____ to spell words right.

4. A strong wind began to _____ across the street.

5. Carl is wearing a _____ shirt today.

6. _____ a circle around the word *tray*.

Word Building

Be a word builder. Double the consonant and add *-ing* to make new words.

Example: flip + p + ing = flipping

7. brag + g + ing = _____

8. drag + g + ing = _____

9. plan + n + ing = _____

10. trap + p + ing = _____

Challenge Extension: Have students write riddles using the words. They may exchange with a partner to answer the riddles.

McGraw-Hill School Division

Words with Blends *bl*, *br*, *dr*, *pl*, and *tr*

Proofreading Activity

There are six spelling mistakes in the paragraph below. Circle each misspelled word. Write the words correctly on the lines below.

Jody liked to drawe. She would plen every picture and trye to make it beautiful. One day I asked her to playe outside, but Jody wanted to color a new picture. Nothing I said could dragg her away from her picture. She colored some cats bright blu. I said, "Cats aren't that color." She said, "I know, but aren't they beautiful?"

1. _____ 2. _____ 3. _____

4. _____ 5. _____ 6. _____

Writing Activity

Make up song titles for silly songs. Use four spelling words in your titles. Circle the words you use.

_____

_____

_____

_____

_____

Words with Blends *bl*, *br*, *dr*, *pl*, and *tr*

Look at the words in each set. One word in each set is spelled
correctly. Use a pencil to color in the circle in front of that word.
Before you begin, look at the sample sets of words. Sample A has
been done for you. Do Sample B by yourself. When you are sure you
know what to do, you may go on with the rest of the page.

Sample A
- Ⓐ onlee
- Ⓑ onley
- Ⓒ only
- Ⓓ onely

Sample B
- Ⓔ cowver
- Ⓕ cover
- Ⓖ cuver
- Ⓗ coaver

1.
- Ⓐ blu
- Ⓑ blue
- Ⓒ bule
- Ⓓ bleu

2.
- Ⓔ blou
- Ⓕ bloe
- Ⓖ bolw
- Ⓗ blow

3.
- Ⓐ brage
- Ⓑ barg
- Ⓒ brag
- Ⓓ bragg

4.
- Ⓔ brass
- Ⓕ bruss
- Ⓖ brase
- Ⓗ brasse

5.
- Ⓐ drag
- Ⓑ drage
- Ⓒ darg
- Ⓓ dragg

6.
- Ⓔ darw
- Ⓕ draw
- Ⓖ drwe
- Ⓗ drawe

7.
- Ⓐ pley
- Ⓑ paly
- Ⓒ play
- Ⓓ playe

8.
- Ⓔ plann
- Ⓕ paln
- Ⓖ plen
- Ⓗ plan

9.
- Ⓐ trie
- Ⓑ tyr
- Ⓒ try
- Ⓓ trye

10.
- Ⓔ trap
- Ⓕ trape
- Ⓖ trp
- Ⓗ trappe

McGraw-Hill School Division

Words with Blends *sl*, *sm*, *sp*, *st*, and *sw*

Pretest Directions

Fold back your paper along the dotted line. Use the blanks to write each word as it is said to you. When you finish the test, unfold the paper and correct any spelling mistakes. Practice those words for the Posttest.

To Parents,

Here are the results of your child's weekly spelling Pretest. You can help your child study for the Posttest by following these simple steps for each word on the word list:

1. Read the word to your child.

2. Have your child write the word, saying each letter as it is written.

3. Say each letter of the word as your child checks the spelling.

4. If a mistake has been made, have your child read each letter of the correctly spelled word aloud and then repeat steps 1–3.

1. _____	**1.** sweet
2. _____	**2.** slide
3. _____	**3.** story
4. _____	**4.** smart
5. _____	**5.** speak
6. _____	**6.** start
7. _____	**7.** slip
8. _____	**8.** spot
9. _____	**9.** swim
10. _____	**10.** smooth

Challenge Words

_____	chance
_____	favorite
_____	heavy
_____	nervous
_____	office

McGraw-Hill School Division

Words with Blends *sl, sm, sp, st,* and *sw*

Using the Word Study Steps

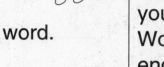

1. LOOK at the word.

2. SAY the word aloud.

3. STUDY the letters in the word.

4. WRITE the word.

5. CHECK the word.
   Did you spell the word right?
   If not, go back to step 1.

Spelling Tip

Use words you know how to spell to help you spell new words. Word beginnings and endings can help. Example:

star + p**art** = start

Find and Circle

Where are the spelling words?

s	w	e	e	t	a	s	b	s	l	i	d	e	h
l	s	t	o	r	y	p	v	w	s	t	a	r	t
i	s	p	e	a	k	o	g	i	t	s	r	m	o
p	w	s	m	a	r	t	s	m	o	o	t	h	v

To Parents or Helpers:

Using the Word Study Steps above as your child comes across any new words will help him or her spell well. Review the steps as you both go over this week's spelling words.

Go over the Spelling Tip with your child. Help your child spell new words by using words he or she already knows.

Help your child find and circle the spelling words in the puzzle.

Words with Blends *sl*, *sm*, *sp*, *st*, and *sw*

sweet	story	speak	slip	swim
slide	smart	start	spot	smooth

Find the spelling words that begin with each of the sounds below. Write the words on the lines.

sl

1. _____

2. _____

sm

3. _____

4. _____

sp

5. _____

6. _____

st

7. _____

8. _____

sw

9. _____

10. _____

Pattern Smart

Write the spelling words that have the same pattern as **spin**.

11. _____ 12. _____

Write the spelling words that have the same pattern as **sweep**.

13. _____ 14. _____

Circle the letters that spell the patterns.

15. Where do these letters appear? Circle the answer.

at the beginning   in the middle   at the end

Words with Blends *sl*, *sm*, *sp*, *st*, and *sw*

sweet	story	speak	slip	swim
slide	smart	start	spot	smooth

Write a spelling word to complete each sentence.

1. Joey is a _____ student and always makes good grades.

2. Be careful not to _____ on the ice.

3. The road was full of bumps, it was not _____ .

4. The candy tastes very _____ .

5. It is time to _____ the test now.

6. My cat has a black _____ at the end of his tail.

7. The teacher read a funny _____ to the class.

Write a spelling word for each picture.

8. _____   9. _____   10. _____

Word Meaning

Be a word builder. Add **ly** to make new words.

  Example: nice + ly = nicely

11. sweet + ly = _____   12. smooth + ly = _____

Write three other words you know that end in **ly**.

13. _____   14. _____   15. _____

Challenge Extension: Scramble the letters in the words and write them on the board. Have students unscramble the words.

Book 2.2/Unit 2
The Wednesday Surprise   15

McGraw-Hill School Division

Words with Blends *sl*, *sm*, *sp*, *st*, and *sw*

Proofreading Activity

There are six spelling mistakes in the paragraph below. Circle each misspelled word. Write the words correctly on the lines below.

A swete little angel lived on a star. The angel knew his star was special. He kept his star very clean so that it would sparkle. The little angel was smarte. He would shine his star until it was smoothe. Then he would sttart to run. Next, he would slipp and sllidde on the star. Living on his special star was fun!

1. _____ 2. _____ 3. _____

4. _____ 5. _____ 6. _____

Writing Activity

Think about your favorite story. Write sentences about why you like that story. Use four spelling words. Circle the words you use.

_____

_____

_____

_____

_____

Words with Blends *sl*, *sm*, *sp*, *st*, and *sw*

Look at the words in each set. One word in each set is spelled
correctly. Use a pencil to color in the circle in front of that word.
Before you begin, look at the sample sets of words. Sample A has
been done for you. Do Sample B by yourself. When you are sure you
know what to do, you may go on with the rest of the page.

Sample A
- (A) blu
- (B) bloe
- (C) bulue
- (D) blue ●

Sample B
- (E) grein
- (F) green
- (G) grene
- (H) grean

1.
- (A) spoat
- (B) spoot
- (C) spot
- (D) spoth

2.
- (E) smart
- (F) semart
- (G) smaart
- (H) smrt

3.
- (A) swimm
- (B) swim
- (C) siwm
- (D) swime

4.
- (E) stoorey
- (F) stry
- (G) storie
- (H) story

5.
- (A) slde
- (B) slied
- (C) slide
- (D) slidde

6.
- (E) smooth
- (F) smoothe
- (G) smoth
- (H) smothe

7.
- (A) speke
- (B) speake
- (C) spoek
- (D) speak

8.
- (E) swet
- (F) sweet
- (G) sweete
- (H) swte

9.
- (A) slip
- (B) silip
- (C) slipe
- (D) slpe

10.
- (E) starte
- (F) strat
- (G) strt
- (H) start

Words with Blends *nk*, *nd*, *ft*, *st*

Pretest Directions

Fold back your paper along the dotted line. Use the blanks to write each word as it is said to you. When you finish the test, unfold the paper and correct any spelling mistakes. Practice those words for the Posttest.

To Parents,

Here are the results of your child's weekly spelling Pretest. You can help your child study for the Posttest by following these simple steps for each word on the word list:

1. Read the word to your child.

2. Have your child write the word, saying each letter as it is written.

3. Say each letter of the word as your child checks the spelling.

4. If a mistake has been made, have your child read each letter of the correctly spelled word aloud and then repeat steps 1–3.

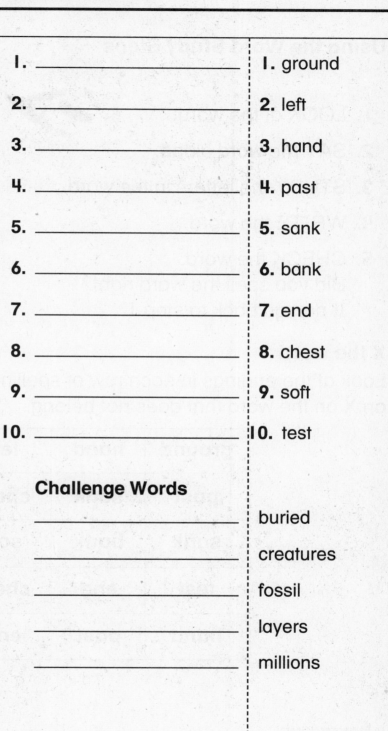

1. _____ 1. ground
2. _____ 2. left
3. _____ 3. hand
4. _____ 4. past
5. _____ 5. sank
6. _____ 6. bank
7. _____ 7. end
8. _____ 8. chest
9. _____ 9. soft
10. _____ 10. test

Challenge Words

_____ buried
_____ creatures
_____ fossil
_____ layers
_____ millions

Words with Blends *nk, nd, ft, st*

Using the Word Study Steps

1. LOOK at the word.

2. SAY the word aloud.

3. STUDY the letters in the word.

4. WRITE the word.

5. CHECK the word.
   Did you spell the word right?
   If not, go back to step 1.

Spelling Tip

Think of a word that rhymes with the new word. Rhyming words often have the same spelling pattern.

s + **ank** = sank
b + **ank** = bank

X the word

Look at the endings in each row of spelling words. In each row, put an X on the word that does not belong.

ground	hand	left
past	sank	chest
sank	bank	soft
test	end	chest
hand	past	end

To Parents or Helpers:
        Using the Word Study Steps above as your child comes across any new words will help him or her spell well. Review the steps as you both go over this week's spelling words.
        Go over the Spelling Tip with your child. Ask if he or she knows other words that rhyme with the spelling words.
        Help your child find and cross out the word that does not belong.

McGraw-Hill School Division

Words with Blends *nk, nd, ft, st*

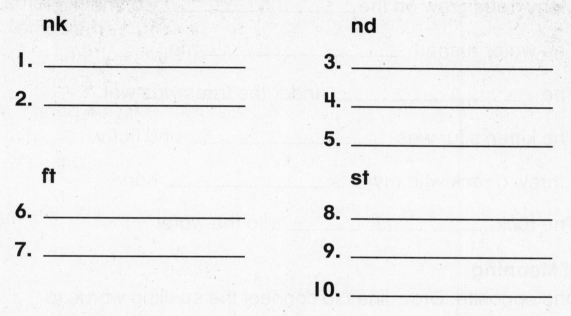

| ground | hand | sank | end | soft |
| left | past | bank | chest | test |

Find the spelling words that end with each of the sounds below.
Write the words on the lines.

nk

1. _____

2. _____

nd

3. _____

4. _____

5. _____

ft

6. _____

7. _____

st

8. _____

9. _____

10. _____

Pattern Smart

Write the spelling words that have the same pattern as **lift**.

11. _____   12. _____

Write the spelling words that have the same pattern as **think**.

13. _____   14. _____

Circle the letters that spell the pattern in each word you wrote.

15. Where do these letters appear? Circle the answer.

at the beginning   in the middle   at the end

Words with Blends *nk*, *nd*, *ft*, *st*

ground	hand	sank	end	soft
left	past	bank	chest	test

Write a spelling word to complete each sentence.

1. Many trees grew on the _____ of the river.

2. The water rushed _____ me.

3. The _____ under the trees was wet.

4. The kitten's fur was _____ and fluffy.

5. I threw a rock with my _____ hand.

6. The rock _____ into the water.

Word Meaning

Find the opposite. Draw lines to connect the spelling words to words that mean the opposite.

Example: hot — cold

7. left   present

8. soft   begin

9. past   hard

10. end   right

Challenge Extension: Have students draw pictures to illustrate words. They may exchange illustrations with a partner to guess pictures.

150

Book 2.2/Unit 2
Fossils Tell of Long Ago

10

McGraw-Hill School Division

Words with Blends *nk, nd, ft, st*

Proofreading Activity

There are five spelling mistakes in the note below. Circle each misspelled word. Write the words correctly on the lines below.

I am writing this note to say hello to people in the future. Then I will put it in a chets. I will bury it in the gruound near my school. I hope people in the future will dig up the note I leftt. They will find out about people in the passt. I will also put in this week's spelling tets.

1. _____   2. _____   3. _____

4. _____   5. _____

Writing Activity

Write a note that will be read one hundred years from now. What do you want to tell people?
Use five spelling words. Circle the words you use.

_____

_____

_____

_____

McGraw-Hill School Division

Words with Blends *nk, nd, ft, st*

Look at the words in each set. One word in each set is spelled correctly. Use a pencil to color in the circle in front of that word. Before you begin, look at the sample sets of words. Sample A has been done for you. Do Sample B by yourself. When you are sure you know what to do, you may go on with the rest of the page.

Sample A
- Ⓐ onlee
- Ⓑ **only**
- Ⓒ onely
- Ⓓ onley

Sample B
- Ⓔ people
- Ⓕ peopel
- Ⓖ peeple
- Ⓗ peple

1.
- Ⓐ sotf
- Ⓑ soft
- Ⓒ soff
- Ⓓ sofft

2.
- Ⓔ bank
- Ⓕ bnak
- Ⓖ bakn
- Ⓗ bannk

3.
- Ⓐ gruond
- Ⓑ grond
- Ⓒ ground
- Ⓓ grund

4.
- Ⓔ tset
- Ⓕ test
- Ⓖ tst
- Ⓗ tets

5.
- Ⓐ letf
- Ⓑ leff
- Ⓒ left
- Ⓓ levft

6.
- Ⓔ end
- Ⓕ enn
- Ⓖ edn
- Ⓗ ennd

7.
- Ⓐ chets
- Ⓑ ches
- Ⓒ chest
- Ⓓ chetts

8.
- Ⓔ hand
- Ⓕ hnad
- Ⓖ han
- Ⓗ hend

9.
- Ⓐ psat
- Ⓑ pas
- Ⓒ past
- Ⓓ passt

10.
- Ⓔ sakn
- Ⓕ sank
- Ⓖ skna
- Ⓗ sanck

McGraw-Hill School Division

Words from Social Studies

Pretest Directions

Fold back your paper along the dotted line. Use the blanks to write each word as it is said to you. When you finish the test, unfold the paper and correct any spelling mistakes. Practice those words for the Posttest.

To Parents,
Here are the results of your child's weekly spelling Pretest. You can help your child study for the Posttest by following these simple steps for each word on the word list:

1. Read the word to your child.

2. Have your child write the word, saying each letter as it is written.

3. Say each letter of the word as your child checks the spelling.

4. If a mistake has been made, have your child read each letter of the correctly spelled word aloud and then repeat steps 1–3.

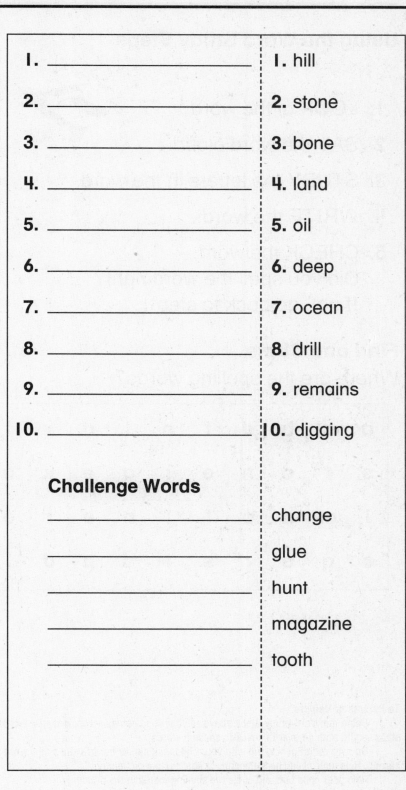

1. _____   1. hill

2. _____   2. stone

3. _____   3. bone

4. _____   4. land

5. _____   5. oil

6. _____   6. deep

7. _____   7. ocean

8. _____   8. drill

9. _____   9. remains

10. _____   10. digging

Challenge Words

_____   change

_____   glue

_____   hunt

_____   magazine

_____   tooth

McGraw-Hill School Division

Words from Social Studies

Using the Word Study Steps

1. LOOK at the word.

2. SAY the word aloud.

3. STUDY the letters in the word.

4. WRITE the word.

5. CHECK the word.
   Did you spell the word right?
   If not, go back to step 1.

Spelling Tip

Think of when you have seen the word before. Think of how it looked. Write the word in different ways to see which one looks correct.
Example:
~~stown~~ ~~stoan~~ stone

Find and Circle

Where are the spelling words?

a	c	b	d	f	h	l	d	r	i	l	l	h	g	j
s	t	o	n	e	i	a	e	k	o	c	e	a	n	n
l	m	n	o	i	l	n	e	r	e	m	a	i	n	s
o	q	e	r	s	l	d	p	d	i	g	g	i	n	g

To Parents or Helpers:
Using the Word Study Steps above as your child comes across any new words will help him or her spell well. Review the steps as you both go over this week's spelling words.
Go over each Spelling Tip with your child. Ask him or her to write a new word in different ways to see which one looks correct. Help your child check the correct spelling in a dictionary.
Help your child find and circle the spelling words in the puzzle.

Words from Social Studies

hill	bone	oil	ocean	remains
stone	land	deep	drill	digging

Write the spelling words in alphabetical order.

1. _____ 2. _____ 3. _____

4. _____ 5. _____ 6. _____

7. _____ 8. _____ 9. _____

10. _____

Pattern Smart

Write the spelling word that has the same pattern as *hand*.

11. _____

Write the spelling word that has the same pattern as *boil*.

12. _____

Write the spelling word that has the same pattern as *peep*.

13. _____

Write the spelling word that has the same pattern as *stains*.

14. _____

Words from Social Studies

hill	bone	oil	ocean	remains
stone	land	deep	drill	digging

All in a Set

Use a spelling word to complete each sentence.

1. Where did your dog bury the _____?

2. Jack and Jill climbed a _____.

3. George liked _____ for treasure.

4. Where will the space ship _____?

5. I like to watch the waves in the _____.

6. Always dive into the _____ end of the pool.

7. Another word for **rock** is _____.

8. Tina put gas and _____ in her car.

9. The worker used a _____ to make a hole.

10. Fossils are the _____ of dinosaurs.

McGraw-Hill School Division

Words from Social Studies

Proofreading Activity

There are five spelling mistakes in the report below. Circle each misspelled word. Write the words correctly on the lines below.

We learned about Columbus in school. We learned that Columbus was very brave. He sailed across the ocaen to find a new ladn. Our class wanted to show our depe respect for Columbus. We wrote a play about him. Then we placed a special stoan on a hille to honor him.

1. _____   2. _____   3. _____

4. _____   5. _____

Writing Activity

Write a story about a dinosaur who visits your school. Use five spelling words in your story. Circle the words you use.

_____

_____

_____

_____

_____

Words from Social Studies

Look at the words in each set. One word in each set is spelled correctly. Use a pencil to color in the circle in front of that word. Before you begin, look at the sample sets of words. Sample A has been done for you. Do Sample B by yourself. When you are sure you know what to do, you may go on with the rest of the page.

Sample A
Ⓐ one
Ⓑ twoo
Ⓒ thwee
Ⓓ foure

Sample B
Ⓔ blu
Ⓕ telo
Ⓖ red
Ⓗ whiite

1. Ⓐ hille Ⓑ hll Ⓒ hill Ⓓ hile
2. Ⓔ bne Ⓕ boone Ⓖ bon Ⓗ bone
3. Ⓐ stne Ⓑ stone Ⓒ ston Ⓓ stoen
4. Ⓔ deep Ⓕ deepe Ⓖ depe Ⓗ deap
5. Ⓐ osean Ⓑ ocene Ⓒ ocean Ⓓ osion

6. Ⓔ oil Ⓕ oel Ⓖ ole Ⓗ oyl
7. Ⓐ drle Ⓑ drill Ⓒ drille Ⓓ drele
8. Ⓔ land Ⓕ lande Ⓖ leand Ⓗ lnde
9. Ⓐ diging Ⓑ degging Ⓒ digging Ⓓ digeing
10. Ⓔ remaines Ⓕ remanes Ⓖ remains Ⓗ remaens

McGraw-Hill School Division

158

Book 2.2/Unit 2
Are You a Fossil Fan?

10

Book 2.2 / Unit 2 Review Test

Read each sentence. If an underlined word is spelled wrong,
fill in the circle that goes with that word. If no word is spelled
wrong, fill in the circle below NONE.
Read Sample A, and do Sample B.

A. I will <u>make</u> <u>pink</u> <u>spice</u> cookies.
         A   B   C

NONE
A. Ⓐ Ⓑ Ⓒ ●D

B. I <u>plan</u> to take a <u>break</u> and <u>rest</u>.
     E   F   G

NONE
B. Ⓔ Ⓕ Ⓖ Ⓗ

1. Bob will <u>come</u> and <u>play</u> in the <u>soft</u> sand.
           A   B   C

NONE
1. Ⓐ Ⓑ Ⓒ Ⓓ

2. The <u>stone</u> and other <u>remanes</u> <u>sank</u> to the bottom.
      E   F   G

NONE
2. Ⓔ Ⓕ Ⓖ Ⓗ

3. At <u>wourk</u> I saw a dog <u>digging</u> for his <u>bone</u>.
      A   B   C

NONE
3. Ⓐ Ⓑ Ⓒ Ⓓ

4. If you're not <u>sick</u>, <u>try</u> to <u>pleay</u> a song.
           E   F   G

NONE
4. Ⓔ Ⓕ Ⓖ Ⓗ

5. I will <u>draw</u> a <u>slide</u> with my left <u>hand</u>.
       A   B   C

NONE
5. Ⓐ Ⓑ Ⓒ Ⓓ

6. Did he <u>try</u> to <u>bragg</u> about how well he can <u>swim</u>?
       E   F   G

NONE
6. Ⓔ Ⓕ Ⓖ Ⓗ

7. Maria was too <u>sick</u> to <u>kome</u> out and <u>play</u>.
             A   B   C

NONE
7. Ⓐ Ⓑ Ⓒ Ⓓ

8. Inside the <u>cheast</u> was a <u>smooth</u> <u>bone</u>.
         E   F G

NONE
8. Ⓔ Ⓕ Ⓖ Ⓗ

9. <u>Try</u> using your <u>hend</u> to <u>smooth</u> the clay.
   A   B   C

NONE
9. Ⓐ Ⓑ Ⓒ Ⓓ

Go on

Book 2.2 / Unit 2 Review Test

10. Please <u>come</u> to <u>play</u> on my <u>sliede</u>.   10. Ⓔ   Ⓕ   Ⓖ   Ⓗ NONE
               E   F   G

11. I <u>brag</u> that I can <u>drow</u> a dinosaur <u>bone</u>.   11. Ⓐ   Ⓑ   Ⓒ   Ⓓ NONE
        A   B   C

12. She will <u>speak</u> about <u>digging</u> for the <u>cheste</u>.   12. Ⓔ   Ⓕ   Ⓖ   Ⓗ NONE
            E   F   G

13. I will <u>bake</u> <u>soft</u> cookies at <u>work</u> today.   13. Ⓐ   Ⓑ   Ⓒ   Ⓓ NONE
           A   B   C

14. <u>Come</u> to the lake and <u>swim</u> to the <u>stone</u> wall.   14. Ⓔ   Ⓕ   Ⓖ   Ⓗ NONE
        E   F   G

15. Don't <u>play</u> ball with a broken <u>boan</u> in your <u>hand</u>.   15. Ⓐ   Ⓑ   Ⓒ   Ⓓ NONE
          A   B   C

16. He may <u>play</u> with the <u>smooth</u> ball in the toy <u>chest</u>.   16. Ⓔ   Ⓕ   Ⓖ   Ⓗ NONE
           E   F   G

17. I will <u>try</u> to <u>draw</u> a picture of the boat that <u>sanck</u>.   17. Ⓐ   Ⓑ   Ⓒ   Ⓓ NONE
        A   B   C

18. Raise your <u>hand</u> if you were <u>diggeng</u> near the <u>slide</u>.   18. Ⓔ   Ⓕ   Ⓖ   Ⓗ NONE
             E   F   G

19. I will <u>swimm</u> in the <u>smooth</u> pool if it is <u>chest</u> high.   19. Ⓐ   Ⓑ   Ⓒ   Ⓓ NONE
          A   B   C

20. Tim hurt his <u>hand</u> but he will <u>triy</u> to <u>play</u> ball.   20. Ⓔ   Ⓕ   Ⓖ   Ⓗ NONE
                E   F   G

McGraw-Hill School Division

Words with Double Consonants

Pretest Directions

Fold back your paper along the dotted line.
Use the blanks to write each word as it is said to you. When you finish the test, unfold the paper and correct any spelling mistakes. Practice those words for the Posttest.

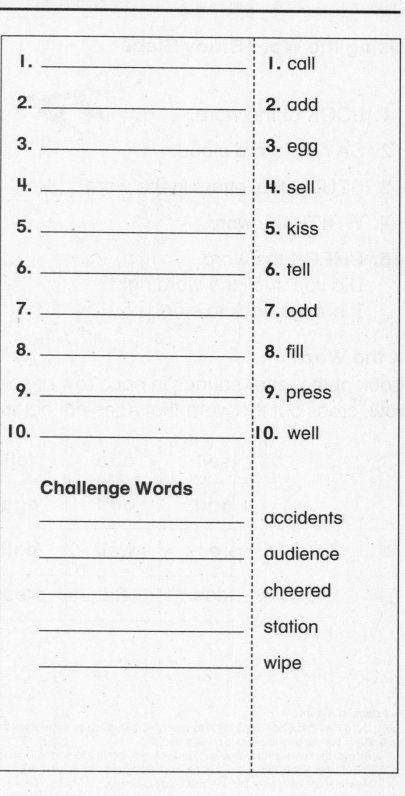

1. _____ 1. call

2. _____ 2. add

3. _____ 3. egg

4. _____ 4. sell

5. _____ 5. kiss

6. _____ 6. tell

7. _____ 7. odd

8. _____ 8. fill

9. _____ 9. press

10. _____ 10. well

Challenge Words

_____ accidents

_____ audience

_____ cheered

_____ station

_____ wipe

Words with Double Consonants

Using the Word Study Steps

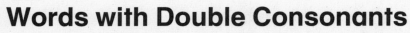

1. LOOK at the word.

2. SAY the word aloud.

3. STUDY the letters in the word.

4. WRITE the word.

5. CHECK the word.
   Did you spell the word right?
   If not, go back to step 1.

Spelling Tip

Add **-s** to most words to form plurals or to change the tense of verbs. Add **-es** to words ending in **x**, **z**, **s**, **sh**, or **ch**.
Example:
    call + s = calls
    kiss + es = kisses

X the Word

Look at the letter sounds in each row of spelling words. In each row, cross out the word that does not belong.

sell	add	tell
add	odd	egg
press	well	call
kiss	fill	press

To Parents or Helpers:
    Using the Word Study Steps above as your child comes across any new words will help him or her spell well. Review the steps as you both go over this week's spelling words.
    Go over the Spelling Tip with your child. Ask him or her to add **-s** to other words to change the tense of verbs. Help your child think of other words ending in **x**, **z**, **s**, **sh**, or **ch** that change the tense of verbs by adding **-es**.
    Help your child cross out the word that does not belong.

Book 2.2/Unit 3
Officer Buckle and Gloria
4

McGraw-Hill School Division

Words with Double Consonants

call	egg	kiss	odd	press
add	sell	tell	fill	well

Match each word with a spelling pattern. Write the spelling word on the line.

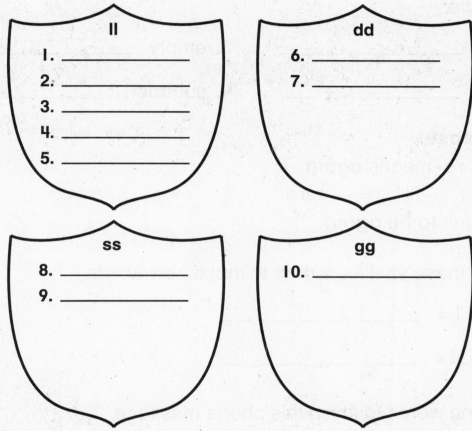

ll

1. _____
2. _____
3. _____
4. _____
5. _____

dd

6. _____
7. _____

ss

8. _____
9. _____

gg

10. _____

Do the Math

Write the spelling word that answers each question.

11. How do you know 2 + 2 = 4? _____

12. How are the numbers 1, 3, 5, 7, and 9 alike? They are

_____ numbers.

Words with Double Consonants

call	egg	kiss	odd	press
add	sell	tell	fill	well

Not the Same

In the space beside each word, write the spelling word that means the opposite.

1. buy _____

2. even _____

3. empty _____

4. subtract _____

Again, please!

The prefix **re-** means **again**.

re + fill = refill

Refill means **to fill again**.

Add **re-** to these spelling words to make new words.

5. re + tell = _____

6. re + call = _____

Use spelling words to finish this phone message.

Hi. It's Amy. Can you _____ me on the phone

later? Please _____ me what time the play starts. I

need to _____ my pants before I go.

_____, I'll see you soon.

Challenge Extension: Have students draw pictures to illustrate each word. They may exchange pictures with a partner to guess the illustrations.

Words with Double Consonants

Proofreading Activity

There are five spelling mistakes in the poem below. Circle each misspelled word. Write the words correctly on the lines below.

> I will not say, I cannot tel,
> What I wished at the wishing weell.

1. _____ 2. _____

> I push and pres but it's a mess.
> The cookie mix is not a success.

3. _____

> I add an eg and hope for the best.
> I'll eat a few and selll the rest.

4. _____ 5. _____

Writing Activity

Imagine that you have an unusual pet. Write sentences about your pet. Use five spelling words in your sentences. Circle the spelling words you use.

_____

_____

_____

_____

_____

Words with Double Consonants

Look at the words in each set. One word in each set is spelled correctly. Use a pencil to color in the circle in front of that word. Before you begin, look at the sample sets of words. Sample A has been done for you. Do Sample B by yourself. When you are sure you know what to do, you may go on with the rest of the page.

Sample A
- Ⓐ will
- Ⓑ whil
- Ⓒ wil
- Ⓓ wille

Sample B
- Ⓔ mis
- Ⓕ mmiss
- Ⓖ miss
- Ⓗ miis

1.
- Ⓐ eeg
- Ⓑ egg
- Ⓒ eg
- Ⓓ egge

2.
- Ⓔ pres
- Ⓕ prest
- Ⓖ press
- Ⓗ pess

3.
- Ⓐ selle
- Ⓑ sel
- Ⓒ seel
- Ⓓ sell

4.
- Ⓔ tell
- Ⓕ tel
- Ⓖ telll
- Ⓗ telle

5.
- Ⓐ fiel
- Ⓑ fiil
- Ⓒ fill
- Ⓓ fille

6.
- Ⓔ call
- Ⓕ kall
- Ⓖ cahl
- Ⓗ calle

7.
- Ⓐ ade
- Ⓑ add
- Ⓒ aad
- Ⓓ adde

8.
- Ⓔ weil
- Ⓕ well
- Ⓖ whel
- Ⓗ weel

9.
- Ⓐ kisse
- Ⓑ kis
- Ⓒ kess
- Ⓓ kiss

10.
- Ⓔ ood
- Ⓕ ohd
- Ⓖ odd
- Ⓗ odde

McGraw-Hill School Division

Words with Digraphs *sh, ch*

Pretest Directions

Fold back your paper along the dotted line. Use the blanks to write each word as it is said to you. When you finish the test, unfold the paper and correct any spelling mistakes. Practice those words for the Posttest.

To Parents,

Here are the results of your child's weekly spelling Pretest. You can help your child study for the Posttest by following these simple steps for each word on the word list:

1. Read the word to your child.

2. Have your child write the word, saying each letter as it is written.

3. Say each letter of the word as your child checks the spelling.

4. If a mistake has been made, have your child read each letter of the correctly spelled word aloud and then repeat steps 1–3.

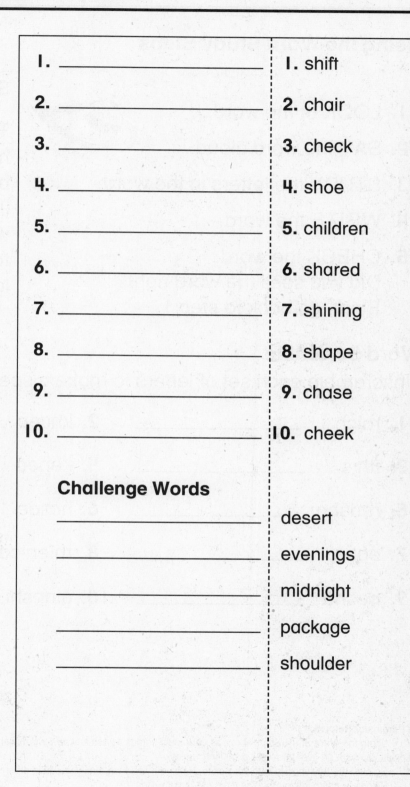

1. _____ 1. shift

2. _____ 2. chair

3. _____ 3. check

4. _____ 4. shoe

5. _____ 5. children

6. _____ 6. shared

7. _____ 7. shining

8. _____ 8. shape

9. _____ 9. chase

10. _____ 10. cheek

Challenge Words

_____ desert

_____ evenings

_____ midnight

_____ package

_____ shoulder

Words with Digraphs *sh, ch*

Using the Word Study Steps

1. LOOK at the word.

2. SAY the word aloud.

3. STUDY the letters in the word.

4. WRITE the word.

5. CHECK the word.
   Did you spell the word right?
   If not, go back to step I.

> ### Spelling Tip
>
> Think of when you have seen the word before. Think of how it looked. Write the word in different ways to see which one looks correct.
>
> ~~shu~~, ~~shoo~~, shoe

Word Scramble

Unscramble each set of letters to make a spelling word.

1. raich _____

2. khcec _____

3. fthis _____

4. kehec _____

5. redsha _____

6. hcsae _____

7. eohs _____

8. rhienlcd _____

9. pesha _____

10. ginnshi _____

To Parents or Helpers:

Using the Word Study Steps above as your child comes across any new words will help him or her spell well. Review the steps as you both go over this week's spelling words.

Go over the Spelling Tip with your child. Help your child write new words in different ways to see which one looks right.

Help your child unscramble the letters to make words.

McGraw-Hill School Division

Words with Digraphs *sh, ch*

shift	check	children	shining	chase
chair	shoe	shared	shape	cheek

Write the spelling words that follow the patterns below.

words with sh

words with ch

1. _____

2. _____

3. _____

4. _____

5. _____

6. _____

7. _____

8. _____

9. _____

10. _____

Word Find

Circle the spelling words in the puzzle.

s	h	i	n	i	n	g	s	h	c
s	s	c	h	a	i	r	i	s	h
h	c	h	e	c	k	s	c	h	a
i	c	h	s	h	i	f	t	a	s
f	h	s	h	a	p	e	s	r	e
c	h	e	e	k	s	h	o	e	m
c	h	i	l	d	r	e	n	d	r

Words with Digraphs *sh*, *ch*

shift	check	children	shining	chase
chair	shoe	shared	shape	cheek

Answer each question with a spelling word.

1. Who plays with toys? _____

2. What can a person sit on? _____

3. What is a part of a face? _____

4. What does a person wear on each foot? _____

Action Words

Draw a line to connect each word with an action the word tells about.

5. check   move from place to place

6. chase   make sure

7. shift   build or create something

8. shape   run after

Word Meaning

Write the base word for each of these spelling words. Remember that some words change their spelling when adding **-ed** and **-ing**.

9. shared _____

10. shining _____

Challenge Extension: Have students work in pairs and create riddles using the challenge words.

Book 2.2/Unit 3
Tomas and the Library Lady 10

McGraw-Hill School Division

Name _____ Date _____

Words with Digraphs *sh, ch*

Proofreading Activity

There are six spelling mistakes in the report below. Circle each misspelled word. Write the words correctly on the lines below.

Our class took a trip to Noisy Brook. Erin tried to chaise a frog, but she fell and cut her cheak. At lunch, all the shildren shareed their snacks. Bobby lost a shoo in the river. He took it off to see how cold the water was. We were lucky that the sun was shyning.

1. _____ 2. _____ 3. _____

4. _____ 5. _____ 6. _____

Writing Activity

Write sentences about a field trip you would like to take. Use four spelling words in your sentences. Circle the spelling words you use.

_____

_____

_____

_____

Words with Digraphs *sh, ch*

Look at the words in each set. One word in each set is spelled
correctly. Use a pencil to color in the circle in front of that word.
Before you begin, look at the sample sets of words. Sample A has
been done for you. Do Sample B by yourself. When you are sure you
know what to do, you may go on with the rest of the page.

Sample A
- Ⓐ chop
- Ⓑ chope
- Ⓒ choip
- Ⓓ schope

Sample B
- Ⓔ yoore
- Ⓕ yur
- Ⓖ your
- Ⓗ yure

1. Ⓐ shayp
   Ⓑ schape
   Ⓒ shape
   Ⓓ shaep

2. Ⓔ children
   Ⓕ childwrn
   Ⓖ childrin
   Ⓗ chilren

3. Ⓐ shifft
   Ⓑ shifit
   Ⓒ chift
   Ⓓ shift

4. Ⓔ chare
   Ⓕ chaar
   Ⓖ chair
   Ⓗ chere

5. Ⓐ check
   Ⓑ sheck
   Ⓒ scheck
   Ⓓ cheke

6. Ⓔ sheek
   Ⓕ cheek
   Ⓖ cheak
   Ⓗ cheke

7. Ⓐ chas
   Ⓑ chass
   Ⓒ chase
   Ⓓ chaes

8. Ⓔ shue
   Ⓕ schoo
   Ⓖ shooe
   Ⓗ shoe

9. Ⓐ shineing
   Ⓑ shining
   Ⓒ schining
   Ⓓ shiening

10. Ⓔ scharred
    Ⓕ shared
    Ⓖ shaired
    Ⓗ shered

Words with Digraphs *th*, *sh*

Pretest Directions

Fold back your paper along the dotted line. Use the blanks to write each word as it is said to you. When you finish the test, unfold the paper and correct any spelling mistakes. Practice those words for the Posttest.

To Parents,

Here are the results of your child's weekly spelling Pretest. You can help your child study for the Posttest by following these simple steps for each word on the word list:

1. Read the word to your child.

2. Have your child write the word, saying each letter as it is written.

3. Say each letter of the word as your child checks the spelling.

4. If a mistake has been made, have your child read each letter of the correctly spelled word aloud and then repeat steps 1–3.

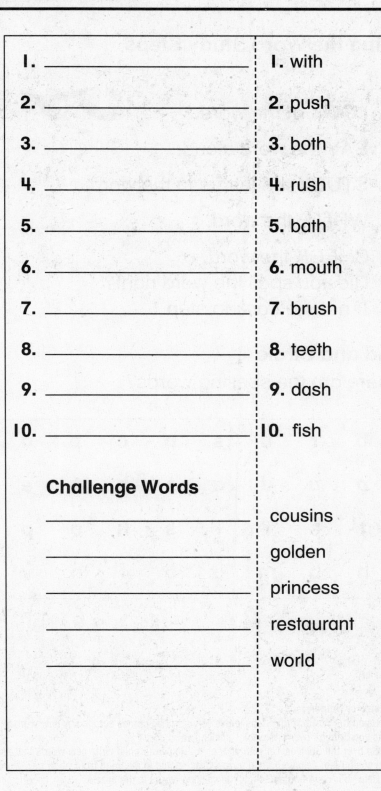

1. _____	1. with
2. _____	2. push
3. _____	3. both
4. _____	4. rush
5. _____	5. bath
6. _____	6. mouth
7. _____	7. brush
8. _____	8. teeth
9. _____	9. dash
10. _____	10. fish

Challenge Words

_____	cousins
_____	golden
_____	princess
_____	restaurant
_____	world

Words with Digraphs *th, sh*

Using the Word Study Steps

1. LOOK at the word.
2. SAY the word aloud.
3. STUDY the letters in the word.
4. WRITE the word.
5. CHECK the word.
   Did you spell the word right?
   If not, go back to step 1.

Spelling Tip

Think of a word that rhymes with a new word. Rhyming words often have the same spelling pattern. Example:

w + ish = wish
f + ish = fish

Find and Circle

Where are the spelling words?

b	r	u	s	h	c	b	a	t	h	f	a
o	u	d	a	s	h	t	e	e	t	h	x
t	s	f	i	s	h	q	p	u	s	h	d
h	h	m	o	u	t	h	v	w	i	t	h

To Parents or Helpers:

Using the Word Study Steps above as your child comes across any new words will help him or her spell well. Review the steps as you both go over this week's spelling words.

Go over the Spelling Tip with your child. Help your child write new words that use beginnings and endings of words he or she can spell. Also, help your child form words related in meaning from other new words.

Help your child find and circle the spelling words in the puzzle.

McGraw-Hill School Division

Words with Digraphs *th, sh*

with	both	bath	brush	dash
push	rush	mouth	teeth	fish

Write the spelling words that follow the patterns in the crowns below.

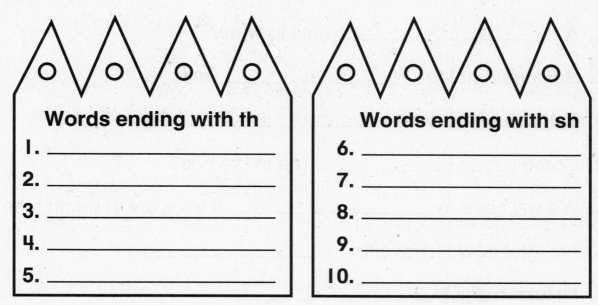

Words ending with th

1. _____
2. _____
3. _____
4. _____
5. _____

Words ending with sh

6. _____
7. _____
8. _____
9. _____
10. _____

Scramble

Unscramble each set of letters to make a spelling word. Write the words. Then circle the two letters that are the same in each word.

11. eehtt _____ 14. oumht _____

12. tohb _____ 15. ithw _____

13. thba _____

Words with Digraphs *th*, *sh*

with	both	bath	brush	dash
push	rush	mouth	teeth	fish

Gone Fishing

Use spelling words to complete each sentence below.

1. A _____ swims in water.

2. Be careful not to _____ me.

3. The fish has a wide _____.

4. Come _____ me in the boat.

5. We will have to _____ if we want to be on time.

6. I'm late; now I'll have to _____.

7. I'll take a quick _____.

8. I'll brush my _____.

9. Then I will _____ my hair.

10. When we are ready, we'll _____ go and dance.

Word Meaning

Synonyms are words that have the same or similar meaning. Write a spelling word that has the same meaning as each word below.

11. hurry _____   12. run _____

Challenge Extension: Have students describe a new restaurant that opened and write a menu for it.

176

Book 2.2/Unit 3
Princess Pooh
12

McGraw-Hill School Division

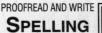
Words with Digraphs *th*, *sh*

Proofreading Activity

There are six spelling mistakes in the paragraph below. Circle each misspelled word. Write the words correctly on the lines below.

The big fishe began to rusch toward him. It wanted to bite him with its sharp teith. What could he do? He waited for the fish to close its big mout. Then he said, "Listen, I don't see why you want to pussh me. There's enough room for botth of us to swim here."

1. _____ 2. _____ 3. _____

4. _____ 5. _____ 6. _____

Writing Activity

What are the girls doing? Write sentences about the picture. Use four of your spelling words. Circle the spelling words you use.

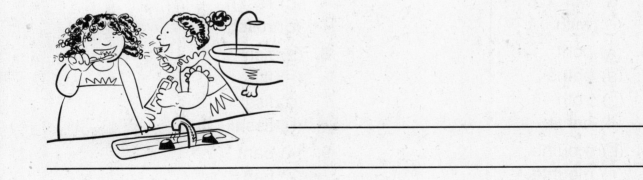

_____

_____

_____

_____

_____

Words with Digraphs *th*, *sh*

Look at the words in each set. One word in each set is spelled correctly. Use a pencil to color in the circle in front of that word. Before you begin, look at the sample sets of words. Sample A has been done for you. Do Sample B by yourself. When you are sure you know what to do, you may go on with the rest of the page.

Sample A
(A) wich
(B) wish
(C) wisch
(D) weish

Sample B
(E) nede
(F) need
(G) neede
(H) neade

1. (A) dash
   (B) dach
   (C) desh
   (D) dassh

2. (E) wiht
   (F) withh
   (G) with
   (H) wiith

3. (A) boht
   (B) bothe
   (C) both
   (D) bohte

4. (E) mouthe
   (F) mouhte
   (G) mouht
   (H) mouth

5. (A) bresh
   (B) bruth
   (C) brush
   (D) brussh

6. (E) teth
   (F) teeh
   (G) teeht
   (H) teeth

7. (A) resh
   (B) rush
   (C) reshh
   (D) russh

8. (E) fish
   (F) fith
   (G) fiss
   (H) fissh

9. (A) baht
   (B) bah
   (C) bath
   (D) bahte

10. (E) pust
    (F) puhs
    (G) pusht
    (H) push

Book 2.2/Unit 3
Princess Pooh
10

McGraw-Hill School Division

Words with Digraphs *th*, *wh*

Pretest Directions

Fold back your paper along the dotted line. Use the blanks to write each word as it is said to you. When you finish the test, unfold the paper and correct any spelling mistakes. Practice those words for the Posttest.

To Parents,

Here are the results of your child's weekly spelling Pretest. You can help your child study for the Posttest by following these simple steps for each word on the word list:

1. Read the word to your child.

2. Have your child write the word, saying each letter as it is written.

3. Say each letter of the word as your child checks the spelling.

4. If a mistake has been made, have your child read each letter of the correctly spelled word aloud and then repeat steps 1–3.

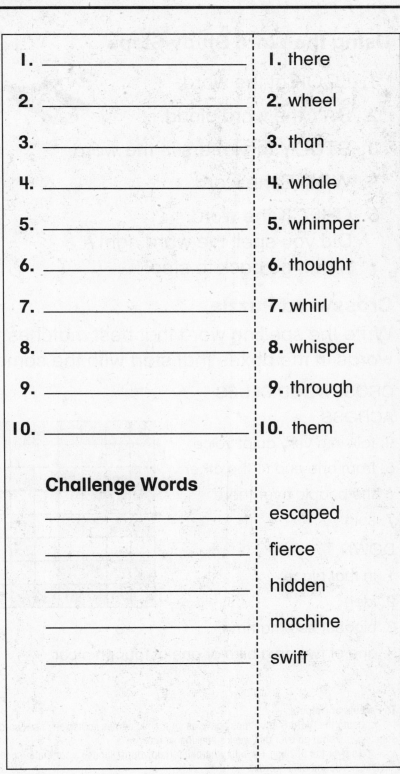

1. _____ 1. there
2. _____ 2. wheel
3. _____ 3. than
4. _____ 4. whale
5. _____ 5. whimper
6. _____ 6. thought
7. _____ 7. whirl
8. _____ 8. whisper
9. _____ 9. through
10. _____ 10. them

Challenge Words

_____ escaped

_____ fierce

_____ hidden

_____ machine

_____ swift

McGraw-Hill School Division

Words with Digraphs *th, wh*

Using the Word Study Steps

1. LOOK at the word.
2. SAY the word aloud.
3. STUDY the letters in the word.
4. WRITE the word.
5. CHECK the word.
   Did you spell the word right?
   If not, go back to step 1.

Spelling Tip

Use words you know how to spell to help you spell new words. Word beginnings and endings can help.
Example:

when + f**eel** = wheel

Crossword Puzzle

Write the spelling word that best matches the clue. Put the spelling words in the boxes that start with the same number.

CROSSWORD CLUES

ACROSS

4. talk in a very quiet voice
5. from one end to the other
6. the people over there
7. spin

DOWN

1. in that place
2. idea
3. biggest sea mammal
4. one of two on a bike or one of four on a car

To Parents or Helpers:
   Using the Word Study Steps above as your child comes across any new words will help him or her spell well. Review the steps as you both go over this week's spelling words.
   Go over the Spelling Tip with your child. Help your child use a computer spell-check feature to learn that it will not catch mistakes in sound-alike words.
   Help your child solve the crossword puzzle.

Name _____ Date _____

Words with Digraphs *th*, *wh*

there	than	whimper	whirl	through
wheel	whale	thought	whisper	them

Write the spelling words that
follow the patterns in the sea
creatures below.

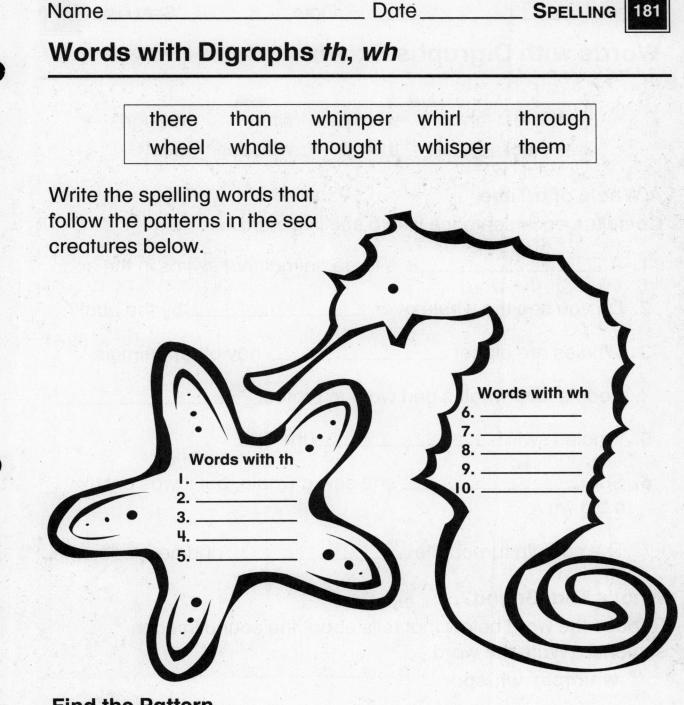

Words with th

1. _____
2. _____
3. _____
4. _____
5. _____

Words with wh

6. _____
7. _____
8. _____
9. _____
10. _____

Find the Pattern

Read each group of words. Circle the word that does not
fit the pattern.

11. thought, than, whirl, through

12. there, whisper, them, than

Words with Digraphs *th, wh*

there	than	whimper	whirl	through
wheel	whale	thought	whisper	them

A Whale of a Time

Complete each sentence with a spelling word.

1. A _____ is a large animal that swims in the sea.

2. Do you see the whale over _____ by the boat?

3. Whales are bigger _____ any other animals.

4. People love whales and want to protect _____.

5. Whales swim _____ the sea.

6. She _____ she saw a whale, but it was only a big wave.

7. The captain turned the _____ and headed home.

What's That Sound?

Choose the word below that tells about the sound in each sentence. Write the word.

whimper   whisper

8. The dog was hurt and started to _____.

9. Susan began to _____ to Martin so no one else could hear her.

10. Which spelling word rhymes with **twirl**? _____

Challenge Extension: Have students draw cartoon characters speaking to each other. They should use the Challenge Words in the dialogue.

McGraw-Hill School Division

Words with Digraphs *th, wh*

Proofreading Activity

There are five spelling mistakes in these
lines from a play. Circle each misspelled
word. Write the words correctly on the
lines below.

Ike: Turn the weel! We want to go over thre by the store.

Ann: I thoght the store was down this street.

Ike: Be careful not to go throogh the yellow light.

Ann: Of course I will. It is better to be safe thaen sorry.

1. _____ 2. _____ 3. _____

4. _____ 5. _____

Writing Activity

Use some of the spelling words to add lines to the play. Tell what
Ann and Ike see or say when they go into a store.

6. Ann: _____

7. Ike: _____

8. Ann: _____

9. Ike: _____

10. Ann: _____

Words with Digraphs *th*, *wh*

Look at the words in each set. One word in each set is spelled correctly. Use a pencil to color in the circle in front of that word. Before you begin, look at the sample sets of words. Sample A has been done for you. Do Sample B by yourself. When you are sure you know what to do, you may go on with the rest of the page.

Sample A
- Ⓐ whath
- Ⓑ whot
- ● what
- Ⓓ whate

Sample B
- Ⓔ play
- Ⓕ plai
- Ⓖ plaie
- Ⓗ plae

1.
- Ⓐ wheal
- Ⓑ wheel
- Ⓒ weel
- Ⓓ whele

2.
- Ⓔ thann
- Ⓕ thane
- Ⓖ than
- Ⓗ tane

3.
- Ⓐ whimper
- Ⓑ wimper
- Ⓒ wimpher
- Ⓓ whimpur

4.
- Ⓔ tought
- Ⓕ thawht
- Ⓖ thout
- Ⓗ thought

5.
- Ⓐ wharl
- Ⓑ whirl
- Ⓒ whurl
- Ⓓ wherl

6.
- Ⓔ through
- Ⓕ thru
- Ⓖ threugh
- Ⓗ threwgh

7.
- Ⓐ whail
- Ⓑ whale
- Ⓒ whal
- Ⓓ whayl

8.
- Ⓔ thier
- Ⓕ tere
- Ⓖ thair
- Ⓗ there

9.
- Ⓐ whisper
- Ⓑ wisperr
- Ⓒ wisper
- Ⓓ wissper

10.
- Ⓔ themm
- Ⓕ thim
- Ⓖ tem
- Ⓗ them

Words From Science

Pretest Directions

Fold back your paper along the dotted line. Use the blanks to write each word as it is said to you. When you finish the test, unfold the paper and correct any spelling mistakes. Practice those words for the Posttest.

To Parents,

Here are the results of your child's weekly spelling Pretest. You can help your child study for the Posttest by following these simple steps for each word on the word list:

1. Read the word to your child.

2. Have your child write the word, saying each letter as it is written.

3. Say each letter of the word as your child checks the spelling.

4. If a mistake has been made, have your child read each letter of the correctly spelled word aloud and then repeat steps 1–3.

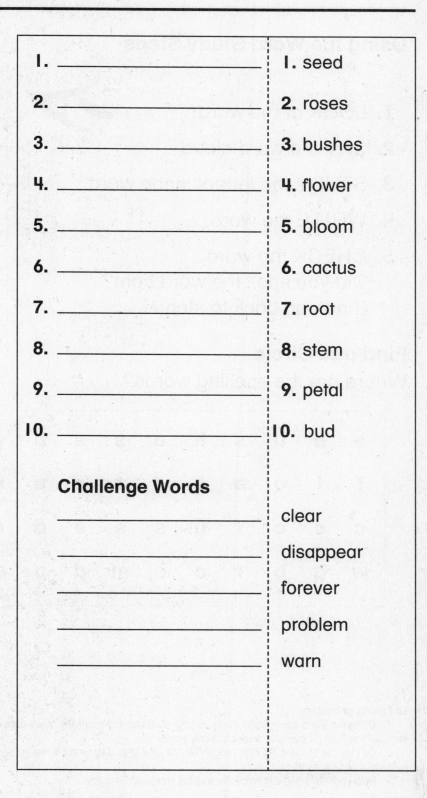

1. _____	1. seed
2. _____	2. roses
3. _____	3. bushes
4. _____	4. flower
5. _____	5. bloom
6. _____	6. cactus
7. _____	7. root
8. _____	8. stem
9. _____	9. petal
10. _____	10. bud

Challenge Words

_____ clear

_____ disappear

_____ forever

_____ problem

_____ warn

Words From Science

Using the Word Study Steps

1. LOOK at the word.

2. SAY the word aloud.

3. STUDY the letters in the word.

4. WRITE the word.

5. CHECK the word.
   Did you spell the word right?
   If not, go back to step 1.

Find and Circle

Where are the spelling words?

e	b	u	s	h	e	s	s	b	y	r	f	g	h
f	l	o	w	e	r	t	e	u	x	o	r	s	t
c	a	c	t	u	s	e	e	d	r	o	s	e	s
w	q	b	l	o	o	m	d	p	e	t	a	l	j

To Parents or Helpers:

Using the Word Study Steps above as your child comes across any new words will help him or her spell well. Review the steps as you both go over this week's spelling words.

Go over the Spelling Tip with your child. Ask your child if he or she knows other one-syllable words ending in one vowel followed by one consonant.

Help your child find and circle the spelling words in the puzzle.

McGraw-Hill School Division

Name _____ Date _____

Words From Science

seed	bushes	bloom	root	petal
roses	flower	cactus	stem	bud

Say each spelling word and tap out the number of syllables. Write the spelling words in the correct flowerpot.

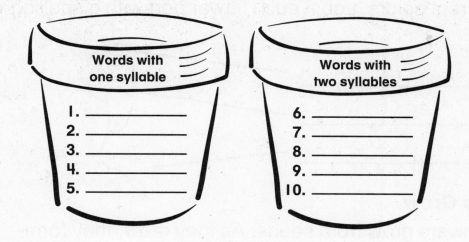

Words with one syllable

1. _____
2. _____
3. _____
4. _____
5. _____

Words with two syllables

6. _____
7. _____
8. _____
9. _____
10. _____

Find and Circle

Where are the spelling words?

y	r	b	u	d	h
j	k	l	e	p	w
f	l	o	w	e	r
u	r	o	s	e	s
a	g	m	i	z	v
c	a	c	t	u	s

Words From Science

seed	bushes	bloom	root	petal
roses	flower	cactus	stem	bud

Flower Parts

Flowers get food through their roots. The stems are green. Petals are different colors. Label each flower part with a spelling word.

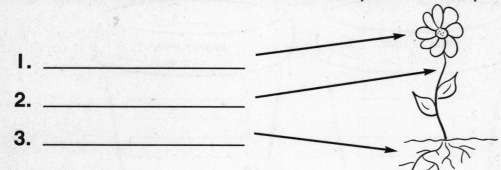

1. _____

2. _____

3. _____

Flowers Grow

Many flowers grow from seeds. As they grow, they form buds. Then the buds open into flowers. Choose the spelling word that correctly names each picture.

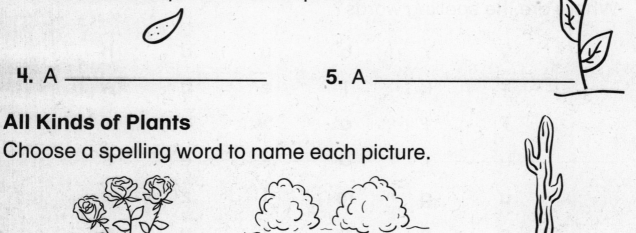

4. A _____   5. A _____

All Kinds of Plants

Choose a spelling word to name each picture.

6. _____   7. _____   8. _____

McGraw-Hill School Division

Challenge Extension: Have students write a fill-in sentence with each Challenge Word. They may exchange papers with a partner.

Words From Science

Proofreading Activity

There are six spelling mistakes in the journal below. Circle each misspelled word. Write the words correctly on the lines below.

July 7   Today, there are many budes on the rose bushis. The rowzis will be in blum by next week, I think. I will be able to cut some pretty flowrs for the house.

July 15   Two weeks ago I planted two new plants. The wind last night broke the steme on one of the plants.

1. _____   2. _____   3. _____

4. _____   5. _____   6. _____

Writing Activity

Pretend that you have a garden. Write a paragraph about how your garden grows. Use four spelling words to describe what happens.

_____

_____

_____

_____

_____

McGraw-Hill School Division

Words From Science

Look at the words in each set. One word in each set is spelled correctly. Use a pencil to color in the circle in front of that word. Before you begin, look at the sample sets of words. Sample A has been done for you. Do Sample B by yourself. When you are sure you know what to do, you may go on with the rest of the page.

Sample A
- (A) need ●
- (B) nead
- (C) nede
- (D) neede

Sample B
- (E) meny
- (F) miny
- (G) meney
- (H) many

1.
- (A) petl
- (B) petel
- (C) petal
- (D) petul

2.
- (E) cactus
- (F) caktus
- (G) cactez
- (H) cactuz

3.
- (A) blum
- (B) blume
- (C) bluhm
- (D) bloom

4.
- (E) seed
- (F) sead
- (G) ceed
- (H) seede

5.
- (A) bede
- (B) bud
- (C) budd
- (D) beud

6.
- (E) bushs
- (F) bushes
- (G) bushiz
- (H) bushis

7.
- (A) rute
- (B) rhute
- (C) root
- (D) ruute

8.
- (E) stem
- (F) stam
- (G) stehm
- (H) steme

9.
- (A) rozes
- (B) rosis
- (C) rosez
- (D) roses

10.
- (E) flower
- (F) flowr
- (G) fower
- (H) flouer

McGraw-Hill School Division

Book 2.2/Unit 3 Review Test

Read each sentence. If an underlined word is spelled wrong,
fill in the circle that goes with that word. If no word is spelled
wrong, fill in the circle below NONE.
Read Sample A, and do Sample B.

A. <u>Will</u> <u>thay</u> come to <u>dinner</u>?
   A B   C

A. Ⓐ ● Ⓒ Ⓓ (NONE)

B. I <u>thenk</u> I will <u>wash</u> my <u>chin</u>.
   E   F   G

B. Ⓔ Ⓕ Ⓖ Ⓗ (NONE)

1. The <u>childrin</u> saw the <u>fish</u> <u>kiss</u>.
     A   B C

1. Ⓐ Ⓑ Ⓒ Ⓓ (NONE)

2. I <u>thought</u> I should <u>adde</u> an <u>egg</u>.
   E   F   G

2. Ⓔ Ⓕ Ⓖ Ⓗ (NONE)

3. I will <u>call</u> you when the <u>rosses</u> <u>bloom</u>.
    A   B   C

3. Ⓐ Ⓑ Ⓒ Ⓓ (NONE)

4. I can't <u>chase</u> the <u>whaile</u> out of my <u>bath</u>.
    E   F   G

4. Ⓔ Ⓕ Ⓖ Ⓗ (NONE)

5. The old woman and all her <u>children</u> <u>shared</u> the <u>shue</u>.
           A   B   C

5. Ⓐ Ⓑ Ⓒ Ⓓ (NONE)

6. <u>There</u> is a time to <u>whisper</u> <u>with</u> your mouth.
   E   F   G

6. Ⓔ Ⓕ Ⓖ Ⓗ (NONE)

7. The <u>stem</u> and the <u>petel</u> are two parts of <u>roses</u>.
    A   B   C

7. Ⓐ Ⓑ Ⓒ Ⓓ (NONE)

8. I <u>shared</u> my silly story about the <u>fesh</u> in the <u>shoe</u>.
   E   F   G

8. Ⓔ Ⓕ Ⓖ Ⓗ (NONE)

9. <u>Call</u> the <u>children</u> to come in for a <u>bath</u>.
   A   B   C

9. Ⓐ Ⓑ Ⓒ Ⓓ (NONE)

Go on →

McGraw-Hill School Division

Book 2.2/Unit 3 Review Test

10. I painted a <u>mowth</u> on the <u>whale</u> with my <u>brush.</u>
       E   F   G
  10. Ⓔ Ⓕ Ⓖ NONE Ⓗ

11. I <u>thought</u> I heard the <u>whale</u> <u>whispur.</u>
     A   B   C
  11. Ⓐ Ⓑ Ⓒ NONE Ⓓ

12. If you draw the flower, <u>add</u> a <u>bloom</u> to the <u>stim.</u>
                      E   F   G
  12. Ⓔ Ⓕ Ⓖ NONE Ⓗ

13. Ben <u>thought</u> he would put a candy <u>petal</u> in his <u>mouth.</u>
       A   B   C
  13. Ⓐ Ⓑ Ⓒ NONE Ⓓ

14. Let's <u>chaise</u> the <u>shoe</u> before we take a <u>bath.</u>
        E   F   G
  14. Ⓔ Ⓕ Ⓖ NONE Ⓗ

15. <u>There</u> is the place to <u>brush</u> mud off your <u>shoe.</u>
    A   B   C
  15. Ⓐ Ⓑ Ⓒ NONE Ⓓ

16. The <u>children</u> found an <u>egg</u> near the bird <u>baith.</u>
         E   F   G
  16. Ⓔ Ⓕ Ⓖ NONE Ⓗ

17. Can I <u>add</u> my <u>thouhgt</u> about getting a <u>fish?</u>
        A   B   C
  17. Ⓐ Ⓑ Ⓒ NONE Ⓓ

18. He will <u>call</u> if he finds my <u>brish</u> and comb <u>there.</u>
          E   F   G
  18. Ⓔ Ⓕ Ⓖ NONE Ⓗ

19. I <u>thaught</u> I would <u>kiss</u> my mom and give her <u>roses.</u>
     A   B   C
  19. Ⓐ Ⓑ Ⓒ NONE Ⓓ

20. Bob <u>shared</u> the <u>egge</u> with the <u>children.</u>
       E   F   G
  20. Ⓔ Ⓕ Ⓖ NONE Ⓗ